Speech Therapy for Toddlers

151 Activities and Games for Optimal Language Development

Table of Contents

Introduction

This book has been written to help you, parents and caregivers, with toddlers struggling with communication; it's full of fun-filled activities and games to ensure children develop their speech and language skills. Communication is the foundation of modern society and critical for success. Therefore, helping children develop the necessary skills is vital to having a well-rounded life. The book focuses on encouraging proper pronunciation, improving vocabulary, encouraging reading, and assisting challenged toddlers through early intervention. It is packed with insights and practical activities to assist those seeking to give their children a good head-start regarding communication.

A child's early life is critical for developing their language skills. Children begin grasping the meaning and use of language in these formative years. When exposed to the right influences, they'll learn to use language to connect with others. They'll see how words act as the lenses through which one can see and understand this little blue dot called Earth and the people they share it with.

However, some children have the misfortune of experiencing delays and impediments that keep them from developing their language skills as quickly and efficiently as they should. Sadly, some parents and caregivers are helpless and unable to do anything about their children's situation because they cannot access the information that could help them. This book has been written to bridge that gap. It aims to assist children in overcoming the challenges of proper communication and language development common in toddlers.

Each activity has been carefully selected to achieve the best results. This tool is for all who seek to assist their little ones with practical advice and fun games, all rooted in evidence-based learning methodologies. It contains information, basic theory, and insights on how a parent can bond better with their child to foster language development in a safe, nurturing space.

To get the most out of this book, parents and their toddlers should practice the activities daily. All explanations for the basic concepts involving speech and language development have been outlined in a way that is easy to understand. The guide explains how children become masters in language use and how parents, caregivers, and therapists can make the language-learning process more efficient for the toddler.

The book also comprehensively addresses most parents' concerns regarding when to contact a speech therapist for help and what to expect from the process. By following the tips in this book, it is easy to create a language-rich environment that fosters the development of communication skills in toddlers.

Constantly engaging in the activities listed in this book will improve a toddler's ability to communicate, enunciate, and understand written and spoken words. Gone are the days when you would hope and pray for the best when dealing with speech impediments. Using this book, loving and attentive parents/caregivers can assist struggling toddlers to express themselves more easily.

Chapter 1: The Basics of Toddler Speech and Language Development

As your little one grows, they eventually learn to speak and communicate with others around them. Speech and language develop with time and practice. During the first three years of your child's life, their mind is open and receptive to ideas. It soaks them up like a sponge, ready and willing to learn as much as possible. During this time, your toddler demonstrates a higher sensitivity to the sounds they can pick up on and the sights around them. They begin to master the art of communication as their world opens up. They now notice language and speech all around them.

Toddlers are more receptive to new ideas.

What makes the phenomenon of mastering language and speech possible for your child? There are specific periods during infancy and early childhood when their mind is fully receptive to language. These periods represent an opportunity to help them blossom in their communication skills. Take advantage of those windows of time to avoid impeding their attempts at communicating fluently and understanding people around them. If you don't, what should otherwise be a smooth journey will be peppered with steep climbs and rugged mountains.

Curious Little Mind

As your child develops, you notice they start to find their voice while playing with it. They learn to express themselves using phrases of two or three words. This self-expression happens between ages two and three. At this time, your little one will have sentences full of curiosity. In other words, they'll ask questions that often begin with why, where, what, or who. You see, they're thirsty for knowledge and understanding. They are essentially a little explorer, an Indiana Jones in their own right, asking questions like "Where is Mommy?" At this time, their vocabulary expands, and they become so proficient in the language that they know at least 200 words. Odds are, they'll know up to a thousand words even. This expansion in vocabulary happens the more they grasp the skill of self-expression.

Your toddler will begin to understand that they are their own unique person. They'll come to identify what makes them different from everyone else. Not only that, but they will express this identity with pride and joy. They are happy to answer the question, "What is your name?" because they understand you're asking about them. They're eager to let you know they're an individual. They have become self-aware, and at this point, you will hear it reflected in their language as they use "me," "I," "my," and "mine." The development of self-awareness is a critical point in linguistic development.

Beyond simply speaking, the child becomes more receptive to language. They master the art of understanding beyond the spoken word. Once they reach age one, they understand commands like "Come here." They realize that the objects they've become familiar with have another dimension called words. They excitedly point at everything around them, trying to enunciate the words that represent them. In their mind, these words are shiny new additions to their world.

You may be worried because your kid is not mastering speech and language at the expected rate, especially for their age. If you notice this, you can't just sit twiddling your thumbs and hope they will improve. It is wise to take them to a professional therapist who can take a look at them and deduce what's going on. Understanding the possible causes of your toddler's delayed speech and language mastery is essential. It could be caused by hearing loss or other issues that typically stunt a child's development. They may need to spend time with a speech-language pathologist or an audiologist if their problem concerns hearing.

As their guardian, there are certain things you can do to help your toddler get better at their linguistic skills. As you go through your daily activities, engaging your toddler linguistically and verbally is a great idea. Talk to them about everything you encounter in a way that will be easy for them to grasp. Talk about the places you go, the books you read, and everything else you do. Sing songs with your toddler. Encourage them to sing along with you, even if they still can't enunciate well just yet. You could read story books together, count, and show them how to emulate you in making animal sounds, clapping, etc. Also, encourage your child by celebrating them every time they successfully imitate a sound or word. By praising them, you encourage them to want to do more.

Understanding the Importance of Language Development

Language development is how your child learns to process speech and share ideas and thoughts through communication. The process is a gradual one. They must first grasp the various verbal and musical patterns inherent in speech. Once they have accomplished this, they can become more fluent as their vocabulary expands. This process remains the same, whether it comes to learning English or Igbo. What isn't always the same, however, is the rate at which toddlers master the spoken word. Various factors can affect how fast and efficient they are at language development.

For one thing, there's the matter of their inherent ability to learn. For another, one child may be more driven to master speech than another. You will also need to consider their environment and how that lends itself to their progress — or doesn't. Why shouldn't you leave their speech and language development to chance? Here are some of the reasons:

Connecting with others: Your toddler's progress with language development matters greatly because this skill enables them to interact with their family, peers, and others around them. Communication isn't only about getting a message across but also about being understood and understanding the other person. Children can only accomplish these things with mastery of language. Yours will find the learning process more manageable if they can understand how to share and receive ideas correctly. When their language development journey is on track, it will be easier for them to socialize with others. They will become a master of interpersonal relations, a precursor for success in any endeavor they decide to engage in as adults.

Bolstering self-esteem: Having excellent language skills improves your child's self-esteem. If you assist them with learning how to work with language effectively, it will drive them to want to connect with the people around them even more. As a result, they will have more confidence in their ability to communicate with others and perform outstandingly at school. Once they have no problems communicating with their peers, they will experience a boost in their self-esteem. It becomes easy for them to establish friendships. Connecting with others and maintaining those connections over time can be highly beneficial in the future. Those relationships are crucial when your child needs help accomplishing their goals and dreams.

Enhancing cognitive skills: Learning a new language improves mental performance. Toddlers become more intelligent and creative as they get better with speech and language. Those with impressive language skills will not have to be concerned about cognitive impairment later in life. Also, it's easier for them to grasp basic ideas useful for learning skills like writing, reading, and listening. In other words, by learning a language, your child will improve their ability to know everything and anything else.

Better literacy: Your child's education should be considered sacred and essential. As they gain mastery over language, their literacy skills develop. They can now unlock worlds of knowledge and enter them through the portals of books. To your child, language is a map that allows them to understand instructions, stories, and any subject material that catches their interest. When they have to master mathematics, it'll be easier for them to understand the language inherent in symbols and numbers. They can only solve mathematical equations by understanding the directions the teacher offers them. Language development is significant to special needs teachers because it helps children learn how to speak and, in the process, have better literacy skills.

Language Development Stages

There are six distinct stages of language development.

1. **The Pre-Linguistic Stage:** Between 0 to 6 months, your child is in the pre-linguistic phase of learning languages. They don't have the needed skills, so they share their ideas and needs with you using sounds. They will coo and cry and murmur to get your attention or get you to do whatever they need since their vocal tracts are still developing. Also, they can recognize specific sounds and voices. Facial expressions and vocal tonality are part of what they consider when you attempt to communicate with them or when they want to reach out to you.

2. **The Babbling Stage:** At this point, your child is likely between the ages of 6 to 9 months. You'll notice they're much more talkative than they used to be. They babble and make other sounds that aren't quite words but seem to be well on their way there. They're growing teeth and muscles in their mouth, which will be necessary for them to say more advanced things.

3. **The Holophrastic Stage:** Once your little one is between 9 and 18 months old, they are in the third development stage. You'll notice that they're much better when communicating. They can say single words that refer to specific needs or objects they're interested in. This is the point where you might expect them to refer to you as "mama" or "dada" to get your attention.

4. **The Words Stage:** They begin crafting sentences of two words that often have an obvious meaning. They may say things like "Thanks, Dad," "More water," "Big cat," etc.

5. **The Telegraphic Stage:** Once your child is between 24 and 30 months old, you'll notice they speak in longer phrases with more than just two words. They may need to improve subject and verb agreement in sentences, but it's easier to understand what they're trying to say now. They grasp simple instructions, such as "Go to the bathroom."

6. **The Multi-Word Stage:** At 30 months, your child is in the stage where they form complex sentences. They're better at communicating their feelings and ideas. They become proficient at understanding when to use the singular form of a word as opposed to its plural.

The following are ways to help your child with their language development:

- Read books to them aloud.
- Have conversations with them.
- Make sure they don't spend too much time on screens.
- Always show them support and encourage them when they use new words or make mistakes.
- Allow them to be in charge of the conversation.

Activities

1. **Mimic Me:** Get your toddler to copy the words and sounds you make. You can start with simple sounds to help them build their confidence and skills more quickly.

2. **Name That:** Show them an object, then help them understand what it's called. It helps to point at the object directly each time you name and describe it – so your baby understands you.

farmer

tractor

sheep

barn

violin

apple

frog

dog

chicken

goose

piglet

goat

duck

rabbit

cow

scarecrow

3. **Sing-Along:** Nursery rhymes are great for helping your toddler master language and improve their vocabulary.

4. **Musical Moments:** For this activity, find a way to incorporate songs into regular everyday moments. When brushing your toddler's teeth, you could sing, "This is how we brush our teeth, early in the morning." This song is great because you can adapt it to anything from tying shoelaces to picking up toys after playtime.

5. **Story Time:** Read easy, simple books to your toddler. As you tell the story, try to be animated and musical. This reading style will help them fall in love with books, inevitably improving their language skills.

Reading to your toddler can improve their language skills.

6. **Ready, Set, Go:** This involves talking them through preparing to head out somewhere. You can talk about tying your tie, putting on shoes, wearing your wristwatch, etc.

7. **Shopping List:** List things you'll buy from the store before heading out. You can show them these objects and name them so they can learn.

8. **Who's Coming?** Discuss who will join you when you go out or whom you want to visit.

9. **Toy Story Time:** For this exercise, you should give them some toys and encourage them to create a story about what they are doing. You can tell the story instead if they still need to learn to speak.

Toy story time can encourage speech development.

10. **Puppet Play:** This exercise requires puppets. Allow them to pretend that the puppet is alive and real, and let them communicate with it while you respond in ways that encourage them to keep talking.

11. **What's That Language?** Depending on how old they are, you could teach them to identify languages by sound. If you don't live in a very diverse neighborhood, you could simply play video clips and have them guess the language.

12. **Direction Detective:** Pick a place your toddler has been to or seen before, and then teach them how to get there. You can make this a visual exercise by walking to the place and back home or getting a marker and some paper out and drawing the way. Have them repeat the directions back to you.

13. **Building Bridges:** If you teach your little one more than one language, you can use objects to bridge them. In other words, you teach them how to say something in both languages.

14. **What Mommy/Daddy Sees:** For this activity, if your home is bilingual, talk about how you see something in one language, and then have your partner talk about how they see it in a different language. This way, your child will become fluent in both languages with time. This practice is the One Parent, One Language strategy, or OPOL.

15. **Rhyme Time:** You and your child should take turns saying words that rhyme. They'll understand phonology, which will inadvertently build their language skills.

Reflection

What improvements have you noticed with your toddler?

How can you reinforce their learning?

Do you notice any signs that worry you?

Chapter 2: The Importance of Early Intervention

Your toddler's growth and development speed cannot be measured in a fixed manner. There aren't specific milestones along the way that they must hit at certain times. Consider it a journey. How your child embarks on it depends entirely on them. Their journey will differ from someone else's because all children are unique. So, applying a cookie-cutter approach to their development and learning is not helpful. Some children walk or talk far earlier than usual, while others take a bit more time. Just because it's taking some children longer than others does not imply there's something wrong with them.

When your child appears to be taking much longer than average to reach certain milestones, like learning their first words or walking, you should seek professional advice. Sure, your child may simply be taking their time to master these things. Still, by seeing a professional, you can make sure they're not facing developmental delays. Those could result from genetic issues, physical conditions, or other environmental factors.

Why Early Intervention Matters

Pediatricians and other professionals can determine if your child is dealing with developmental delays and offer a roadmap to help them. Early intervention involves assessing whatever issues they may be struggling with as soon as possible. The emphasis on time exists because the sooner you identify the problem, the easier it'll be to correct it. Your little one's brain is highly plastic and malleable, so it is best to address developmental issues while they're young.

Pediatricians can determine if your children are facing developmental delays.
https://www.pexels.com/photo/a-physician-examining-her-patient-8460030/

If your child struggles with language development and speech, early intervention implies working with a speech and language skills pathologist. This pathologist gives them exercises and playful activities that will help them master language and better interact and communicate with others around them. Children get early intervention from age three if they show signs of developmental delays or are at risk of it. Getting them the help they need is not optional, as it is set in stone in <u>Part C</u> of the <u>Individuals with Disabilities Education Act</u>. This act ensures every child can access early intervention services across all states.

Among the many professionals your child may need are speech-language pathologists, audiologists, occupational therapists, physical therapists, special educators, and psychologists. You do not necessarily have to engage with all these professionals at once. Your child's needs will dictate who you need to see at every point.

Developmental Skills

There are five significant categories of developmental skills to be concerned about. **Cognitive skills** are all about thinking, solving problems, and learning. These skills are essential because they help your child understand how the world works, how to make good decisions, and how to read and solve math. **Communication skills** involve listening, talking, understanding, and gesturing. These skills are required because they need to be able to express their needs, connect with others, and learn. **Physical and sensory skills** are vital for motor tasks like climbing, walking, and crawling. They're also necessary for helping them understand sensory information such as hearing and seeing. These skills are the foundation they'll build on as they engage with their environment and participate in social interactions.

Social-emotional skills involve understanding how people feel, play, and make friends. With these skills, your child will better understand themselves and how to create excellent, positive relationships with others. They are also necessary for them to successfully navigate society in an individual period.

Finally, there are **adaptive** or **self-help skills,** which involve basic things like getting dressed, showering, having a meal, etc. Early intervention ensures children will have no issues with these skills.

Signs and Symptoms of Speech or Language Issues

LANGUAGE DEVELOPMENT

How children learn to talk in one or more languages

SOUNDS:
BIRTH TO 5 MONTHS

Follows what you say from day one
Cooing (aaaah, oooh, grr)
Smiles

SYLLABLES:
6 TO 12 MONTHS

Starts recognizing simple words
Raspberries (trills with the lips)
Babbling (bababa, wadawada)
First word (ball, bye-bye)

WORDS:
12 TO 18 MONTHS

Understanding: ca. 140-190 words

Production: ca. 75-112 words

SENTENCES:
18 TO 48 MONTHS

Understands two-step directions
and more abstract concepts
Vocabulary spurt
Basic grammar (Dad sleeping)
Increasingly complex sentences

META-LINGUISTICS:
48+ MONTHS

Understands everything, incl. figurative language
Combines sentences
Rhymes
Takes listener's perspective

Suppose you have concerns about your child's development, especially hearing, language, and speech. In that case, it's only natural to be worried. However, understand that they are unique and will develop independently. You should, however, know the signs that your child is having difficulty in these areas so you can offer support early if needed. What do you do if you suspect something more is going on?

First, identify the signs. Usually, children will master skills between 12 and 18 months. However, a child taking much longer than that could imply a problem. From birth to about three months, your child should begin smiling and playing with others around them. From 4 months to 7 months, they should be babbling. From 7 to 12 months, they make sounds and gestures. These gestures could include pointing or waving. They demonstrate they understand what others say when they're anywhere from 7 months to 2 years old. From 12 months to 18 months, their vocabulary is bigger than before.

When your toddler is one and a half years old to 2 years old, it should be easy for them to put at least two words together that make sense. They'll have a vocabulary of above 50 words by age two. They enjoy talking and playing with the other children from ages two to three. They can handle basic writing and reading from two and a half years to 3 years. If your child doesn't like looking at books or drawing, that could be a sign that something is wrong. You may need to enlist the services of a professional.

Look out for speech sound disorders. Speech refers to the way you say words and make sounds. Typically, your little one will mispronounce things. There are certain sounds they may only pronounce once they hit ages four to six. However, the following are ways to deduce whether your child has speech sound issues. From age one to two, more often than not, your child should be able to pronounce P, B, M, H, and W correctly when they appear in words. They can usually pronounce K, G, F, T, D, and N correctly from ages two to three. When your child is that age, and it isn't easy to understand when they speak -- even for the people they live with -- that could indicate a problem.

Stuttering is another sign to look out for. Often, people will repeat a sound or word or pause during speech. There's nothing wrong with that. However, if you notice this happens far too often, it may be a *stutter*. Your child may initially stutter as they master the language, which is nothing to panic about. Over time, their stutter will go away. However, there are signs that it may be there to stay. If your child is between the ages of two and a half to three years, ask yourself the following:

- Do they have trouble pronouncing words?
- Do they tend to repeat the first syllable in words?
- Do they pause too often when they speak?
- Do they stretch out sounds (especially the first one) in a word?

If you answered yes to any of these questions, odds are your child is struggling with a stutter and will need help from a professional.

Voice disorders are another issue to watch for. When you don't use your voice correctly, it can change. If you're not feeling well, or you've been yelling or talking too much, you can lose your voice. You'll know your child has a voice disorder if you notice that their voice is always breathy, scratchy, or sounds like they've screamed themselves hoarse. Another voice disorder your child may struggle with is talking through their nose.

Pay attention to signs of hearing loss. Unfortunately, some children lose their hearing at birth, while others gradually lose it the older they get. If your child struggles with hearing loss, you may notice the following things:

1. From birth to one year old, your child may ignore the noises around them.
2. From seven months to one year, they may never respond when you call their name.
3. When your child is one to two years old, they do not follow simple instructions.

As bad as all these situations sound, never give up on your child or lose hope. You should take advantage of early intervention. Get help when you notice something wrong instead of waiting and hoping for the best. You can find low-cost or even free services that will assist your child to have the best shot at life. So, do not hesitate to speak with a professional or your doctor. They can tell you what early intervention programs are available in your area.

Benefits of Early Intervention

1. Expect better communication skills. Your child's ability to speak clearly will help them express their needs and feelings better.
2. They will do far better academically. They'll understand what's taught in class and engage with their teachers and peers.
3. They'll have a chance at healthy, positive relationships. Early intervention will make them develop socially and emotionally as they should. This development, in turn, will feed their sense of self-worth.
4. Your child will have more independence than those who didn't get the help they needed because they will be able to better express their needs.
5. You decrease the odds of them having speech difficulties in the future. They won't struggle with being understood, nor will they need therapy for the trauma they'd have to deal with if they felt constantly misunderstood.

Activities

16. **Sound Snacks:** When your toddler is snacking, have them associate each food with a specific sound they must pronounce before eating.

Associating sounds with snacks can help your toddler learn about sounds.
https://unsplash.com/photos/mP8HvwFA_dw?utm_source=unsplash&utm_medium=referral&utm_content=creditShareLink

17. **Chatterbox Chimes:** You'll need wind chimes for this. Assign a word, phrase, or sound to each chime, and have your toddler say the word when the chime sounds.

18. **Tale Trails:** For this, you'll need several toys. Then, have your child mimic how each toy would speak one after another to create a story.

19. **Magic Mimic:** You'll need a pair of magic wands. When you say a word, act like you're casting a spell. Then, have your child copy you as they repeat the sound.

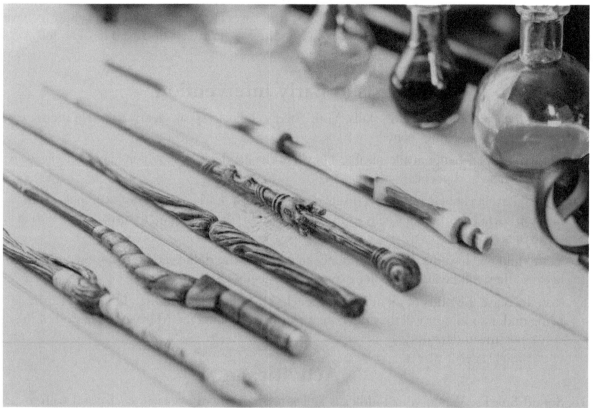

You'll need magic wands for magic mimic.
https://www.pexels.com/photo/wooden-sticks-on-white-wooden-table-7978779/

20. **Rhyme Rocket:** Tell them you will build an imaginary rocket made of rhymes. Another part is added to the missile when your toddler says a word that rhymes with yours. You can pretend to blast off into space when you have a chain of ten rhymes. You could also just draw the rocket while mimicking missile launch sounds.

21. **Animal Anthems:** You can make up songs about different animals and have your toddler sing with you.

22. **Puppet Parleys:** This is almost like puppet play, except you'll need at least two. Let them talk to each other while your toddler watches.

23. **Gesture Games:** Assign a word to a gesture. Your toddler must say the correct word whenever you make that gesture.

24. **Word Wagon:** This is just like the Rhyme Rocket, but you'll be building a wagon with words. You and your toddler can add a wheel for every correct word. You could create a three-wheeled wagon or go nuts and create one with ten. It's up to you both!

25. **Sound Scavenger Hunt:** This is a scavenger hunt, but your toddler only gets clues when they correctly pronounce a sound or a word.

26. **Picture Pronunciations:** You'll need picture books to make this work. All your toddler needs to do is say the names of the objects in the book.

PICTURE PRONUNCIATIONS

APPLE

CLOCK

HOUSE

WHEEL

DAISY

WATERMELON

LAPTOP

CLOWN

AMBULANCE

MONEY

LEMONS

DOG

27. **Babbling Bubbles:** Blow bubbles, and for each one, make a sound or say a word your little one has to repeat before they get to pop it or before you blow a new one.

28. **Echo Echoes:** This is an echo game. You say something, and your toddler has to say it back. Begin with simple words and sounds, then add an extra syllable as you continue.

29. **Tongue Twisters:** You need to develop tongue twisters that involve the sounds your child needs to improve on making.

30. **Rhythm Rattles:** You need a rattle for this. Shake it in the rhythm you want your child to use to pronounce a word, then let them try.

Reflection

What have you noticed about your toddler's speech that worries you?

Has there been a dip since the last time you tracked their progress?

In what ways could you make speech therapy more fun for your child?

Chapter 3: Establishing a Language-Rich Environment

What is a Language-Rich Environment?

A language-rich environment is one where your child has many opportunities to be exposed to language, stimulating their desire to learn and interact using that language. This setting is the best condition to place your toddler in if you want them to master their speech and language skills, especially if you've noticed they're struggling in some way or are a little behind on the timeline for language skill development. In this environment, children are exposed to a vast vocabulary, engaged in exciting conversations to model conversational flow, and more. Other things that make an environment optimal for developing language skills include narrating daily tasks while doing them, reading aloud, singing, using playful rhymes, and asking them open-ended questions that get them to say more.

The Importance of a Language-Rich Environment

The first three years of your child's life play a crucial part in their language development because, at this point, their brain develops rapidly and takes in a lot of information. That will assist them tremendously as they work on their literacy skills.

Another reason to ensure your toddler is in a language-rich environment is that it enables them to develop a broad and impressive vocabulary. They learn new expressions and words with ease. They'll understand how to use those expressions and their meaning across contexts. The more words your child hears, the more their vocabulary will grow, making it easier for them to express themselves. In a language-rich environment, they are exposed to proper grammatical structures and learn how the rules of the language work implicitly. With time, they'll begin using these correct structures in everyday speech.

Understand that language involves both communication and cognitive development. The better your little one uses languages, the better their attention, memory, and cognitive abilities are. By immersing them in a world of words, you encourage them to learn how to make plans, fix problems, and grasp more complicated concepts than others may be used to at their age.

Here are other advantages your toddler will enjoy:

- They'll develop excellent social skills, such as taking turns when talking with others.
- They'll understand the nuances in language, which change depending on social contexts.
- They'll learn how they can use language to develop connections with others.
- They'll master how to express their feelings effectively.
- They'll develop a deeper understanding of what others around them think.
- They will also develop emotionally to communicate their needs and handle their feelings readily.

When learning a language, repetition is vital. So, do all you can to ensure your child is in an environment where they are repeatedly exposed to phrases and words. They'll then be able to use words correctly in the proper context. Also, they'll learn to pronounce and articulate words accurately, which is crucial when developing speech skills. You can always create a language environment to help your child with specific issues. If they have trouble pronouncing particular sounds, you can set up an environment where you emphasize and repeat sounds.

Setting Up the Environment

First, make sure that you have a structured environment. This way, your child will find it easy to understand what's happening, and they'll be able to anticipate what's happening next. You create a structured environment by using consistent rituals, rules, and routines. You should also consider designating specific spaces for specific activities. If you'd like your little one to read, you should have a quiet, cozy place that facilitates the process of reading and concentration.

Next, take advantage of visual supports. Consider working with picture schedules, labels, and charts. Using these makes it easier for children to understand what is expected of them when transitioning from one activity to the next and the routines they are to work with every day. These visual aids are excellent for introducing new words to your child and helping them reinforce the knowledge of the ones they already have learned. You may want to label everyday items in the home or the class so they can master how to spell and pronounce these words with ease.

Work with interactive displays. You can set up displays on the wall around the home or the classroom, ideally at your child's eye level. By using these displays, you encourage them to engage with them. The interactive nature of the displays you choose will make things interesting for them and accelerate the rate at which they learn. Consider an alphabet chart with textured letters or a weather chart. Your child can assign the correct weather symbols for the day. Another great display to work with is a storyboard, which allows them to move the pieces around to create exciting stories.

Books and other reading materials are essential. Consider getting a good set of age-appropriate books and magazines for your child. The books you choose should be books that have pictures and engaging stories. Make sure that it is easy for your toddler to reach them. When they read regularly, they can connect words on paper. They also understand how they sound and what they mean. Reading allows your little one to learn new vocabulary and understand story structure easily.

Language activities and games are excellent tools for crafting a language-rich environment. Consider memory games, puzzles, bingo, word matching, etc. You can also work with toys and encourage them to use their imagination and start conversations.

Make sure that the space allows your child to interact with others. When it comes to learning language, children flourish when they are socializing with others. Schedule time each day for your child to engage in group activities. Consider setting up classroom discussions or scheduling a play date with a good friend of theirs. Role-playing is also a fantastic way to help them practice telling stories and conversing with others engagingly.

Do your best to keep noise to a minimum. If you hope to give your kid the best shot at learning language and speech, keep the noise to a minimum. If their environment is noisy, they may feel distracted and overwhelmed, and it'll be more challenging for them to pay attention and understand whatever you say to them.

Offer your child a rich multisensory environment. The more their senses are engaged in the learning process, the better they will learn. Say, for example, you're teaching your little one the meaning of "rough." Having them touch something rough but safe would be a great idea. If you're teaching them about the word "sour," you can let them taste a bit of lemon or lime. This process will establish strong connections between the words and their meanings. Also, they will be more likely to remember what they have learned.

Encourage them to express themselves. Use storytelling, drawing, painting, dancing, running, etc. By encouraging your child to express their thoughts and ideas, they'll get much better at using language.

Show your child the proper use of speech. When you talk, enunciate. Use a variety of words, and always complete your sentences. If you make an incorrect sentence or pronounce something wrong, correct yourself so your child can learn. Also, when they use the wrong phrases, do your best to correct them, but be gentle about it. Positive reinforcement will go a long way toward helping them to communicate better. As you encourage them, you help them feel more confident and motivated to improve their speech.

Take advantage of technology. Several useful apps are available to help them develop their language skills and speech. These apps are interactive and engaging, so your toddler will have a blast learning how to speak correctly.

Taking Advantage of Everyday Routines

Daily routines are excellent opportunities for your little one to learn to speak correctly. When you have a meal, that is a perfect chance for them to learn new words and how to use them properly. The words will obviously be associated with food, cooking utensils, and actions such as eating, spooning, stirring, etc. As you enjoy a meal together, you can talk about the color, texture, and taste of what you're eating. Don't just talk to your toddler. Instead, engage them in conversation. Ask them open-ended questions to get them to say more words about the meal.

Bath time is another excellent time to teach your toddler new words, especially those connected to washing and rinsing. They can learn what hot and cold mean. You can show them the differences between being dry and wet. You can teach them about body parts. Make this more interesting by incorporating songs as you bathe your little one or wash their hair.

Other everyday routines excellent for teaching them new words include getting dressed to head out, playtime, walking outdoors, and a bedtime routine. When getting dressed, you can talk about the colors and the various items of clothing they will interact with. When walking outdoors, you can talk about the weather, nature, shops, and anything they can hear, see, or feel. As for bedtime, you can read them a book and talk about the stories, pictures, and exciting characters.

Activities

31. **Whispering Winds:** This is a way to teach your child to speak softly and hear soft sounds. Have them pretend they're in a library and must be quiet as they echo your words.

32. **Story Stones:** These stones have various pictures on them. You and your little one can pick a stone, one after the other, and tell a story based on the image.

33. **Treasure Box:** Fill a box with different toys and other objects. You and your child should take turns pulling something out of the box, naming it, and then saying something about it.

Take turns pulling out toys and naming them.
https://www.pexels.com/photo/ethnic-boy-reaching-out-to-braided-box-6624269/

34. **Action:** For this game, you demonstrate verbs like "sleeping," "jumping," "eating," and so on, and then your little one has to say the correct word to identify the action.

35. **Wonderful Weather:** Talk about the weather every day with your toddler. Use vivid descriptions.

36. **Sound Safari:** Take them on an imaginary safari. Here, each animal has its sound. Make the sound and have them copy you. This game is a great way to help your child learn animal sounds and imitation.

37. **Finger Painting Phonics:** Get a piece of paper and write some letters of the alphabet. Let your child paint over them while pronouncing the sounds of each one.

38. **Funny Faces:** Sit with them in front of a mirror and make exaggerated faces to represent different emotions. Have your child make those faces while teaching them what each one means with words like "sad," "happy," "surprised," and so on.

39. **Dance and Describe:** Dance to some music with your toddler, then pause it at intervals and describe the movements you're making. Have them do the same.

40. **Laughing Letters:** Get your child a stack of letter cards to identify each letter. When they get something right, you should both laugh together.

41. **Feel and Find:** Get a bag and put objects of various textures in it. Let your toddler reach into it without looking at the contents. They should feel around, grab something, and do their best to identify it. This game is an excellent way to teach them descriptors like "hard," "squishy," "soft," etc.

42. **Colorful Commentary:** You'll need toys of various colors to play with. Blocks are a great option. If your child wants a toy or a block to create something, have them name the color before you hand it over.

43. **Picture Peekaboo:** Get a picture book your toddler loves, cover most of it with a sheet of paper, and expose only a small part. They need to guess what the picture might be. This game is used to build their imagination and description skills.

44. **Sound Shadow Birds:** You need to be in a dark room. Whatever sound you make, have your child repeat it. If they repeat it correctly, turn on a flashlight, link your thumbs together at the base with your palms facing you, and then let your hands cast a shadow on the wall. The shadow will resemble a bird. Flap your hands to make it fly, then turn off the light and do a new word.

45. **Musical Words:** You'll need a drum or any other percussive instrument. Pick a category of words, such as foods, colors, emotions, or animals. Your child should say a word in that category whenever you play the drum or other instrument.

Your child should say the word after you hit the drum.

Whatever you do, make sure your child is having fun. Don't pressure them into being perfect. Make it an enjoyable time and understand that mistakes along the way are acceptable and even encouraged.

Reflection

How would you rate the language-rich environment you've created at home for your toddler?

What changes could you immediately implement to improve your child's linguistic environment?

Are there any hindrances to learning that you may need to eradicate?

Chapter 4: Interactive Language Games

Whether you're an adult who's figured out the basics of life or a child still growing and learning, play is essential. Your toddler needs play to develop because it helps them interact with the world around them and fosters their creativity. When children play, they become fascinated by the world and the many things it has to teach them. It's not just about giving them a break from academic rigors. Play gives your child the structure they need to thrive cognitively and socially. It is one of the best ways to become fluent in a language. You know by now that when your toddler experiences a delay in language and speech mastery, this will hurt their interactions with others, their behavior, and their capacity to do well in academics. Leverage the power of play to help your child become a well-rounded individual.

The Skill of Play

Playing will enable toddlers to handle complex experiences.

There are many ways your child can play. Each form of play has its unique benefit. As they grow older, their play skills will take on new dimensions, enabling them to handle new, more complex experiences and ideas. For an infant, playing is about exploring the world around them. This form allows them to develop sensory-motor skills. You can tell they're engaged in this form of space when they throw their toys around or suck or chew on them. You may not have thought about this much, but this teaches your little one about cause and effect. They learn that actions have consequences by throwing their toys around. They also understand that things happen sequentially.

As your child grows, the power of playing becomes even more evident. At this point, they no longer engage in nonverbal communication. Now, their form of play requires imagination. You notice they like to play dress up or pretend. They want to imitate others around them in speech and behavior. This phase of play is essential because it allows the development of conversational and language skills. If they struggle with shyness, interactive play that involves imagination is a great strategy to help them become more confident.

The Influence of Play on Language Development

Ages ago, people assumed that learning and playing shared no connection. However, it is now clear that they are intricately linked. Play is essential for academics because it makes learning easier for your child. It offers the chance for your child to get better at using language. Think of little things like asking their friends if they'd be willing to share a toy or telling you they're tired. The seemingly inconsequential steps are essential for developing language in their formative years.

Playing collaboratively with their peers will help your child with language. It will allow them to be more articulate and understand how people use language in everyday experiences without feeling pressured to be correct. As your child gets better at interacting with their peers, they'll also become more comfortable. They'll open up to share their inner world with others around them. If you want to take advantage of this, allow your child to play outdoors. That enables them to explore the world and investigate whatever piques their curiosity. They'll ask questions, and as a result, they will realize the importance of speaking up and questioning what they do not understand.

When your child plays alone, they learn to notice their surroundings and pay attention. The more they pay attention, the better they concentrate for long periods. Concentration leads to developing strong listening skills. Solitary play is also a great way to gain insight into how your little one thinks.

Like most parents, you would be concerned if your child could not communicate effectively in school. A simple solution would be to encourage them to play more. Something about playing makes children speak up better and louder. Even when your child isn't playing with others but is engaged in parallel play, you'll notice that their communication skills improve. Encourage them to be close to friendly peers, and you'll notice them open up more and express themselves confidently.

Developing a Positive Attitude to Speech Therapy with Play

Play is an excellent way to help your toddler lower their inhibitions. When a child realizes that they are receiving instructions or someone is evaluating their performance, it intimidates them. They feel pressured in this situation. When the environment is very formal, such as doing a speech therapy session, they are even more aware of their limitations. So, play is an excellent way to combat this feeling of pressure.

Creating a safe environment for your child to play in is essential because safety means comfort. They don't feel like everything they say or do is overly scrutinized in this space. This safe feeling will allow them to play with language and make mistakes freely as they learn. By creating an environment that helps them play, they know it's okay to fail. Feeling free, they are more at ease trying new words and phrases. They know no one will reprimand them for making mistakes. This way, they're more willing to explore and take risks. By using play, you can positively reinforce their progress. Reward them whenever they get something right, and they'll feel more comfortable, confident, and willing to learn.

Play for Engagement and Motivation

Speech therapy requires time and patience. Ensuring that toddlers remain engaged throughout the process is quite a challenge. The best way to keep up their motivation is by using play. When speech therapy is rooted in space, your little one finds the process fun. They're oblivious to the fact that they're working on getting better. This way, they remain interested in whatever tasks you give them.

Where other therapy methods require a child to be passive, play-based speech therapy gets them involved and invested. They're not just sitting there waiting for instructions to carry out. They feel like they are carried along in the process. This is great because they will develop a sense of ownership and autonomy, which are excellent for keeping their motivation up.

You can even work rewards into the process of play. Whenever your child does a specific task or hits a new milestone, you should offer them something to mark the occasion. When they know they will be rewarded for their effort, they easily maintain their good spirits and want to continue with therapy.

Activities

46. **Sound Puzzle:** Give your toddler a few objects or toys in a box. Each one should represent a sound. Have them reach into the box, pick a toy, and then make the sound you assigned to it.

47. **Feel and Say:** You'll need textured papers or cards. Have your child touch the paper, and then describe how it feels to you with various adjectives.

48. **Letter Leapfrog:** Draw a hopscotch grid. Instead of using numbers, you use letters. Have your child hop on one foot to each note on the grid, and then say a word that begins with that letter before jumping to the next.

LETTER LEAPFROG

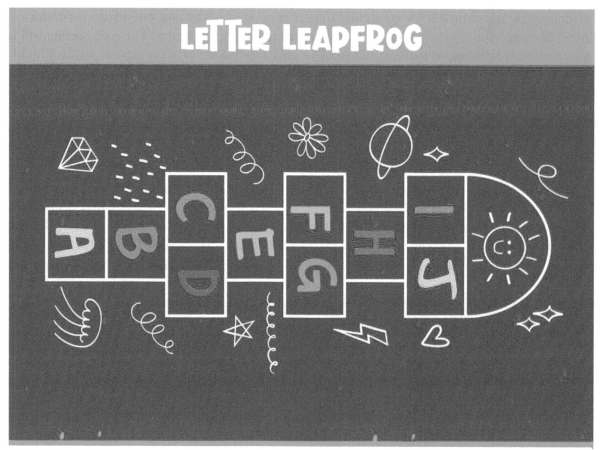

49. **Silly Sentences:** You'll need a stack of cards for this one. Each card should have a unique word on it. You and your toddler should take turns drawing the cards and then creating sentences with the words in them. If you want to have more fun, make the word sillier.

50. **Guess the Object:** Blindfold your child. Put a toy or an object in their hand. They must guess what they're holding based on touch alone. When they get it right, have them describe other things they notice about it.

51. **Synonym Search:** Pick a random word. They need to develop as many synonyms for that word as possible. They can also use phrases that are synonymous with the word.

52. **Charades with Sounds:** Play a game of charades – but instead of acting out a word, act out a sound. You could bark like a dog, rev like a car engine, etc. Let them figure out what you're imitating and tell you.

53. **Rhyming Hopscotch:** Draw a hopscotch grid. This differs from Letter Leapfrog because your child has to come up with a word that rhymes with the word you give them before they can hop on to the next square on one foot.

54. **Story Dice:** You'll need a pair of dice with words, objects, settings, or characters on them. Roll the dice and develop a story based on whatever shows up. Then, encourage your child to do the same. This will do wonders for their narrative and creative thinking skills.

IDEAS FOR STORY DICE

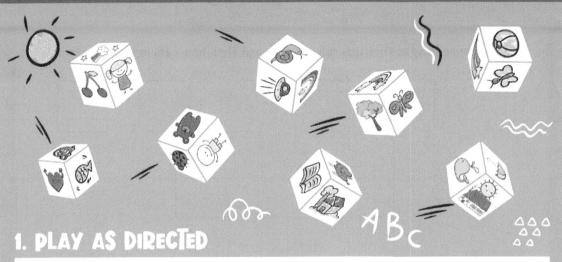

1. PLAY AS DIRECTED

The storyteller rolls all 9 dices. Begin with 'Once Upon a Time' and tell a story that links together all 9 face-up images. Start with the first image to grab your attention. Use three dices for the beginning, three for the middle and three for the end of the story. There is one rule: there are no wrong answers.

2. USE ONE DICE

Rather than using all 9 dices, you could place all dices into a bag and choose one dice at random and then tell a story using all six images on one dice.

3. TALL STORIES

A different approach to storytelling is to use all the dices from all the series and start putting one on top of the other. You roll all the dices or pick one out of a bag/box and continue the story putting more and more dices on top of each other. The story ends once all the dices collapse, then the next player continues with the same rules above.

4. GUIDED STORIES

You can use the following template to create personalized story. There are three key areas: the introduction of the characters, the decision to go on a journey to achieve something and then returning back home to live happily ever after.

STORY DICE: GUIDED STORY

Draw the nine images that you rolled below and then name them In brackets below

[ ] [ ] [ ] [ ] [ ] [ ]
(_____) (_____) (_____) (_____) (_____) (_____)

[ ] [ ] [ ]
(_____) (_____) (_____)

Once upon a time, there was a 1_____ who lived in a
2_____. One day the 1_____ wanted to
3_____. He visited a friend, 4_____, to help. They
both decided to travel to 5_____ and brought a magic
6_____.

During the trip to 5_____, they suddenly saw a
7_____. Both the 1_____ and the
4_____ used the magic 6_____ to help.
Afterward,
they continued their journey to 3_____.

Once they arrived at 5_____, they met a 8_____.
The 8_____ told them that they must give the magic
6_____ if 1_____ wanted to
3_____.
1_____ gave the magic 6_____ to
8_____.

Both 1_____ and 4_____ traveled back
2_____ with the help of a 9_____ and they
were so
pleased as 1_____ could do 3_____. And they lived
happily ever after.

55. **Phonetic Photo Album:** You'll need to create a photo album with different pictures. The word representing each picture should begin with a different sound than others. Your child needs to go through each picture in the album and name it.

56. **Vocabulary Volcano:** Write a few words on different pieces of paper. Crumple each piece so it resembles a rock. Let them make the volcano erupt by choosing a rock, straightening it out, and reading the word within the rock.

57. **I Spy Sounds:** This is a game of I Spy, but instead of objects or colors, you focus on sounds. You could say, "I can hear with my little ear, something that starts with the letter b." They would then have to guess that you're talking about a bird.

58. **Word Tower:** Get some building blocks and write various words on the sides. Your child needs to stack these blocks to create words and then say the words they create out loud.

59. **Opposite Day:** Tell your child it's Opposite Day. Each time one person says a word, the other person must say the opposite word. For example: tall/short, happy/sad.

60. **Sound Garden:** Work with popsicle sticks or craft sticks for this one. Write various words on them. Get your child to plant these sticks in a pot of soil as they pronounce the words on each one.

The sound garden helps your children pronounce words better.
https://www.pexels.com/photo/building-a-box-from-colorful-craft-sticks-10282712/

61. **Word Wheel:** Create or get a spinning wheel. Stick different words on the wheel. Your child's job is to spin the wheel; wherever it stops, they must say the word it lands on.

62. **Emotion Thesaurus:** Sit with your child and discuss various emotions, and then both of you have to come up with as many words as possible to describe each emotion.

Reflection

Which of the activities did you find most effective for your little one?

What was their level of engagement during the activities?

What specific games would you like to use more often to help them?

Chapter 5: Improving Vocabulary

Why Improving Your Toddler's Vocabulary Matters

There are so many critical reasons to help your toddler master the use of language and improve their vocabulary. For one thing, you help them develop as they should. For another, you give them a chance to succeed in life. Here are more reasons to take time to help them use more words and do so correctly.

An improved vocabulary means they'll communicate effectively. Vocabulary is the foundation of all languages and cannot be avoided. When your child has an arsenal of words, they'll never be at a loss when expressing their ideas and feelings. They can be clear in their messages, and everyone will be able to understand exactly what they mean. Being understood is a validating experience that improves their self-confidence. This boost in confidence is also excellent for setting them up for future success in whatever they choose as a vocation.

Your toddler will experience rapid cognitive development. Vocabulary growth is connected to cognitive growth. The more words your toddler masters, the better they'll be at categorizing things correctly, making the proper associations, understanding what the world is about – and even more importantly – *understanding themselves.* The ability to understand one's self is essential for critical thinking, which is a valuable skill to have. Also, when your child becomes an adult, they'll be experts at solving problems quickly.

Giving them the best vocabulary means they can express their emotions and regulate them. When your toddler has the words required to share how they feel accurately, it can make them feel less frustrated when things go awry. Letting off some steam about an undesirable situation (even if they can't change their circumstances) is a good thing that calms them. Remember: they're like you in some ways, but they're still little humans.

Their social skills also get a boost from an improved vocabulary. The fact that your toddler knows what they want to say and *how* to say it will make it easier for them to connect with their peers. Their interactions with others will be much smoother, so they'll become masters at making friends and keeping them. In life, the importance of cooperating with others cannot be overstated. So, by ensuring your toddler has a stellar vocabulary, you give them a fighting chance at learning how to interact with others productively.

A great vocabulary means reading readiness. Improving your toddler's vocabulary will make them better prepared to read. It will be much easier for them to understand the words in books since they've heard them before and used them in different contexts. Reading readiness is necessary so your child can do well in school and later in life.

A great vocabulary means success in academic work. The earlier you start teaching your child more words, the more likely they will do well in school. They'll have excellent reading and writing skills. So when it's time to go to school, you can be sure that your child has a headstart and will perform phenomenally well.

You can boost your child's self-esteem and confidence by helping them with their vocabulary. When they find it easy to communicate their ideas, they're more inclined to want to participate in conversations. In school, they'll want to answer questions and share their thoughts. This ability will help them feel good about themselves and improve their confidence.

They'll have a better shot at learning new languages. You're giving them the tools they need to learn any other language later on, as they can find the parallels between their spoken language and others. Inadvertently, this will lead them to be more empathetic and understanding of others.

Give your child a robust vocabulary if you want to stop them from experiencing delays in their language development. Help them as early as possible and address whatever issues pop up swiftly, and you'll give them the best shot at mastering speech on time.

Fuel their curiosity as you show them how to use new words. The more their vocabulary grows, the more questions they'll have about life, and the deeper they'll want to get into various subjects. Curiosity may have killed the cat, but it's beautiful for children to be fascinated by the world around them.

Do all you can to help your toddler improve their vocabulary, and they'll thank you for it later. A vast vocabulary will do wonders if you want them to excel in writing, reading, speaking, *and listening*. It's easy to see how this can be wonderful for their school and future success. Your child's vocabulary size in kindergarten is an excellent predictor of how well they will learn reading. To improve their vocabulary, treat it as a marathon, not a sprint. This process kicks off in infancy and continues all through their life. It's never too early to expand your toddler's vocabulary.

Pretend Play for Better Vocabulary

Playing pretend is vital to your child's development for a good reason. They work with their imaginative and creative abilities each time they play pretend. They develop their language and vocabulary. So, encourage them to take on different scenarios and roles. You'll notice their contextual use of language improving by leaps and bounds.

When children play pretend, they copy the actions and words of the adults around them. Vocabulary is heavily dependent on the roles that they choose to play. If they're pretending to be an astronaut, a chef, or a doctor, it's natural to choose the language that aligns with those roles. Pretend play creates a space of zero judgment and 100% safety. In this space, your toddler can enjoy working with new words. They can infuse these words into their speech and play with them to discover the various contexts in which they can use them.

When your toddler is engaged in pretend kitchen play, they are immersing themselves in an environment rich with language. They're learning to "cook" and "serve" meals. They're learning what it means to "chop," "boil," "stir," and "plate" meals. They can now tell what the "oven" is and what the "microwave" does. They are learning all the vocabulary that involves the skill of cooking and working with the necessary utensils. This way, they build their vocabulary.

In the same way, when your toddler enacts a situation of visiting the doctor, they learn words such as "bandage," "stethoscope," "thermometer," and what it means to "take your temperature." They "listen to your heart." If it's a grocery shopping situation, your child learns about the different quantities and kinds of food and how much the items cost. If your child is interested in computers, a pretend scene of them hacking into a mainframe is a great way to teach them the language associated with that area of interest. It's easy to see how helpful pretend play is. It's flexible and adaptable to your child's interests or needs.

They don't need to pretend-play alone; you can be present and guide your child's playtime so they can master more complex language. You can model new phrases and words for them to copy. You can note any errors your little one makes and gently teach them the correct use of the term that they got wrong. Also, you can offer positive reinforcement whenever your child finally uses something they've been struggling with correctly.

Open-Ended Questions

When you have a meaningful conversation with your toddler, you create an environment rich in language. They get better at using language and improving their vocabulary. One of the methods you can use to enhance your conversations with them is to use open-ended questions. See that you give them enough time to respond to your questions. Also, help them expand on their responses by coaxing them to say more or sharing your perspective and asking them what they think.

You can't answer open-ended questions with just "yes" or "no." They encourage your child to take time and think through your thoughts. They'll have to give you a complex answer, meaning they will use more complex language. Don't ask your child if you had a good time at the park. Instead, ask them what the best part was about visiting the park. This question prompts them to take time and think through their answer.

Give your child enough time to answer. Remember, you have more mastery over your language than they do. They'll need more time to process your question. They have to reach within themselves to notice how they feel. Then, they translate those feelings and thoughts into a correct response. So, take your time and be patient with them as they try to answer. Rushing them will undermine their confidence; *this will not improve their language development.* Demonstrate to them that you value their thoughts by waiting. By doing that, you show them you are actively engaged and interested in what they share. In turn, they'll be encouraged to be more expressive.

Building on your child's answer is another excellent strategy for improving their vocabulary. You can model how to use new words in their correct contexts. If they say, "I saw a big cat," you could build upon that sentence by saying, "It was a big, brown cat in a tree. It was a Maine Coon." By answering in this way, your child has learned the words "brown," "tree," and "Maine Coon." You've also shown them that their answers can be more detailed.

Repetition and Reinforcement

To improve your toddler's vocabulary, you should use repetition and reinforcement. These two tools are essential in helping your child learn new words. They are necessary for memory retention. By repeating and reinforcing new words, the child conceptualizes how to use those words in everyday situations.

Repetition is about presenting the same word or phrase to them in various ways. The more often they hear it, the stronger the neural pathways in their brain become. They will be able to make the connection between the word you use, what it means, and the contexts in which to use it in correctly.

Repetition is excellent for helping your child remember and recall the word and its meaning when they want to use it. It increases the chances of your child wanting to use that word in their speech. However, it's not enough to just hear the word. Let them listen to it used in various situations, sentences, and contexts. This way, they can be more versatile in using that word.

Reinforcement is about helping your toddler associate the words they just learned with the meaning of the words over and over again with time. The more you do this, the more you cement the word's purpose in your child's long-term memory. You can reinforce these words using tactile, visual, and auditory methods. To achieve repetition and reinforcement, you can weave these words into your everyday routine to make learning an organic process for them. Consider using these new words when you read, have a meal, or play together. Also, look for opportunities to point out events and objects connected to the new word your little one learns when you head out for a walk or a drive.

10 Practical Tips for Improving Your Child's Vocabulary

Read together. Pick books that are perfect for your child's age. They should have illustrations that will engage their attention. As you read aloud, they'll learn new words and how to pronounce them correctly. They'll learn new concepts and how to structure their sentences properly.

Narrate everything you do. It doesn't matter if you're taking out the trash or cooking. Talk about what you're doing. If you're peeling some potatoes, you could say, "Now, I'm peeling potatoes for dinner." You could also point out things that would be interesting things around your toddler to help them identify objects with ease.

Work with word banks. You could have a word of the week or day. Explain what the word means to your toddler in a way that is easy for them to understand, and then use it all through the day in various sentences. You could pin the word to your fridge or somewhere central where your toddler will read it often.

Use interactive conversations. Engage your child in dialogue by using open-ended questions to get them talking. It doesn't matter if they can't fully flesh out a sentence. Just ask them, and they'll be eager to answer you. You could ask them, "What did you do in school today?" That should get them talking.

Be descriptive in your language. You can use synonyms for words you usually use with them. Instead of using the word "big" repeatedly, you could say "enormous," or "huge," or "gigantic." This way, you improve their vocabulary and give them even more adjectives to work with.

Engage them with songs and rhymes. Music is an excellent way to grab your little one's attention and get them to learn new words. The great thing about rhymes and songs is they encourage repetition, which is excellent for your child to remember the new information you're exposing them to.

Use pretend-play and role-playing. You can work with dolls. If your toddler prefers action figures, use those instead. Even better, you can both use your imagination to create *pretend scenarios.*

Work with educational apps. You should be mindful of giving them too much screen time, but that doesn't mean you shouldn't take advantage of educational apps and games that make learning new words fun for your child.

Take them on outings and field trips. You could take them to the park, museum, zoo, or garden. These places offer great opportunities for your child to learn new words related to paintings, animals, plants, etc.

Share stories. You can tell a story and then have your toddler tell you one. The story doesn't have to make sense, and it doesn't have to be long, either. You just want them to work with the words they know and master how to sequence events in proper narrative structure.

Activities

63. **Chef's Kitchen Vocabulary Challenge:** This is a pretend cooking activity. Your child will learn the names of various utensils, ingredients, and cooking actions. Have them name their ingredients whenever they cook something and discuss the process.

64. **Doctors Clinic Word Checkup:** This game is excellent for teaching your little one medical terms in a fun way. Have them pretend they're a doctor. They have to use the proper names for each medical tool and procedure.

65. **Grocery Store Word Hunt:** For this game, have your child pretend they've got a shopping list. They need to walk through an imaginary store to find the required items on the list. You can print pictures on paper and put them on the wall. In this way, they will learn about the various food items.

66. **Astronaut Space Lingo:** If your child is interested in outer space, have them pretend to be an astronaut. You can introduce them to words such as gravity, planets, rocket, asteroids, etc.

67. **Zoo Explorers Animal Talk:** Your child is a pretend zookeeper or visitor for this activity. In this game, they'll learn about the different animals in the zoo, their sounds, their behaviors, what they like to eat, and other exciting things. This game offers you a plethora of words to teach them.

68. **Storytelling Showdown:** Start telling a story for this game, then stop in the middle and have your child add to it. You'll encourage them by using open-ended questions such as, "What happens next?" This activity is a great way to expand their vocabulary.

69. **Question Chain Train:** You and your toddler should take turns asking open-ended questions about any topic you want. Say you want to talk about water. You could ask questions like where can you find water? Or why is the ocean salty?

70. **Word Building Blocks:** This game will teach your child how to build sentences. Have them start with a simple sentence, then expand on what they've said. This activity is how you show them how to use new phrases and words. Take turns expanding on sentences.

71. **Wonder Why Wheel:** Create a wheel with different subjects. Have them spin the wheel. Whatever topic it lands on, ask them open-ended questions about it. Remember to give them enough time to answer and to expand on their responses by adding new information and words.

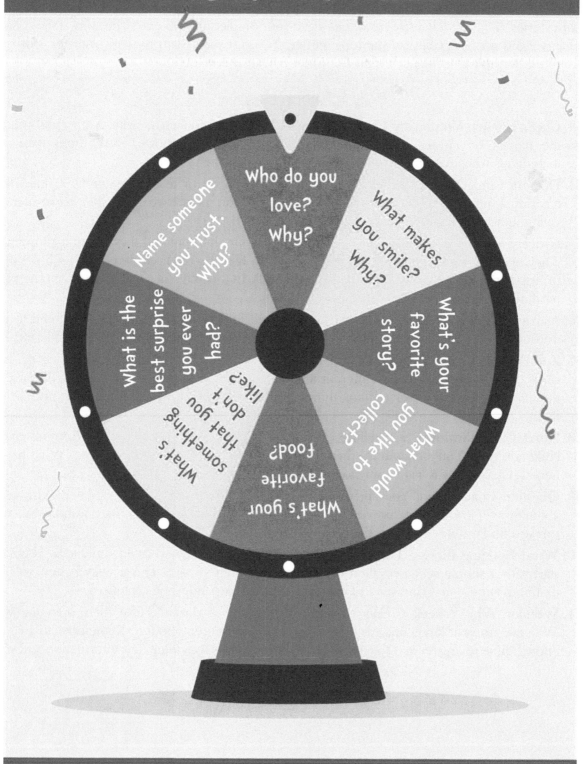

72. **Fact or Fiction:** This is a fun game where you share a statement with your little one, and they must deduce whether it's fact or fiction. If they're unsure, encourage them to ask you open-ended questions so they can learn more and come up with the answer. In this way, you encourage them to be more inquisitive and learn to use language to get more information.

73. **Word of the Day Relay:** Pick a word of the day. All through the day, look for opportunities to use that word. Encourage your toddler to do the same.

74. **Vocabulary Hunt:** Take walks with your toddler daily and turn those walks into a vocabulary hunt. You should have a list of words you've recently taught them. Make a game of finding things connected to those words around you as you walk.

75. **Picture Word Match-Up:** You will need flashcards with pictures on one side and the words that describe them on the other. These are excellent for teaching your child storytelling, matching, and improving their memory. You can show them the picture and have them say the word, or show them the word and let them describe the image that should be on the other side.

76. **Rhyme Time:** Incorporate the new vocabulary or words you have taught your little one into songs or rhymes. Since songs for toddlers tend to be repetitive, they're excellent for helping them retain new information.

77. **Word Wizard:** This is an imaginative game. Choose a new word, say it out loud, and both have to imagine the word appearing in thin air. After this, you can use the word in various sentences or act out in different situations to help your child visualize it contextually.

Reflection

What words have you noticed your toddler is most interested in?

What was your toddler's response to the activities in this chapter?

What aspects of their vocabulary would you like to help them build better?

Chapter 6: Supporting Speech Sounds: Phonetic Focus

Understanding Phonetics

Your toddler needs to understand phonetics to use sounds correctly in whatever language you want them to speak. Regarding their language development, it's about picking up distinct sounds and replicating them. These sounds are called phonemes. In the English language, there are 44 of them. Your child begins to pick up on these distinct sounds because they're born with that ability. With time, as they continue to interact with language, they get better at using the phonetics specific to the native language they speak. They can tell the different sounds across various languages at six months. At twelve months, they become a specialist in their native language and can no longer tell the subtle differences between the phonemes in other languages. This process is known as perceptual narrowing.

Your toddler can learn a language and develop their skills thanks to the early period when they pick up on phonetics. That phase is critical. It's how they know words and can tell them apart. Not many people realize this, but it's quite a feat when a child can tell the difference between the words "bat" and "dat," the latter being nonsensical. The fact that they've developed a phonetic understanding makes it easy for them to become literate. They can tell that "d" represents the /d/ sound, and "b" represents the /b/ sound.

Phonetics and Speech Clarity

Every parent wants their toddler to speak clearly and intelligibly. Understanding the phonetic elements of a language is helpful in this regard. Early on, your baby plays around with different sounds as they try to work out how to use their vocal tracts as well as you do. They try to work their jaw, lips, and tongue to make these sounds. As they grow older and interact with the environment around them, they get better at pronouncing these sounds. The child has listened to you enough times that they've become better at doing so.

When your toddler masters phonetics in their language, they can move on from just babbling random sounds that aren't language-specific to using actual words that mean something. Every language has its phonemes. They can begin to speak intelligibly and fluently when they can replicate them accurately. They pick up the patterns and tones inherent in a language and can tell which syllables should be stressed in a word or phrase. For them to speak clearly, they must understand how to pronounce individual sounds and string them together to talk naturally. Think of the way English is structured. How you pronounce a sound depends on the sounds that come before or after it. This interesting phenomenon is known as coarticulation.

Phonemic awareness begins with segmentation, where your child can break words into separate sounds. Say your child learns that the word "bat" comprises the individual sounds /b/, /æ/, and /t/. The next element is blending, where they listen to a sequence of phonemes spoken individually and then combine them to create a word. Isolation is another aspect that matters. It's about being able to tell what the individual sounds are in the word. The final element of phonemic awareness is addition and deletion, where your child learns that they can switch the "b" in bat to a "c" and get a new word. Thanks to phonemic awareness, toddlers can learn to read and spell correctly and match various sounds to their written equivalents through phonics.

Phonetic Disorders

Suppose your toddler has issues articulating properly or understanding the sound system of the language you're teaching them. In that case, odds are they're struggling with phonetic disorders. Two kinds of disorders could be the problem: articulation or phonological disorders.

Articulation disorders: This sort of disorder involves physical struggles with making certain sounds. Articulation disorders show up when your little one distorts words, uses one sound instead of another, or leaves out a sound from a word. Think about when children say "wabbit" instead of "rabbit."

Phonological disorders: These disorders show up as a pattern of errors in sounds, like when they say "dah" instead of "dog" because they tend to do away with the last consonant (final consonant deletion). The errors tend to affect several sounds.

So, how do you address these problems? First, these disorders must be spotted and diagnosed. A speech-language pathologist can evaluate your child. They will deduce where the toddler's skills are in terms of speech and language. They'll conduct an oral-motor assessment, a hearing test, a speech production inventory, and a phonological analysis. Once your child has been diagnosed, there should be therapeutic interventions. The speech-language pathologist will craft a tailor-made treatment plan for your child. When the issue is an articulation disorder, the treatment will teach them how to produce the sounds they struggle with physically. They'll show your toddler how to place their lips and what shape they should be in. If it's a phonological disorder, the treatment will involve explaining the rules of phonology using games and other exercises.

By constantly practicing, your child can overcome phonetic issues. You could encourage them to pronounce the sound they struggle with or combine it with other sounds, words, sentences, and regular speech. When they get it right, positive reinforcement will drive them to want to practice more to get even better. To help them even further, make sure you make speech practice a daily thing. Work it into daily activities. Also, check in with the speech-language pathologist to ensure the strategies work and your child progresses.

Phonetics and Music

Phonetics and music share a connection. When you combine the two in speech therapy, your toddler's language development improves significantly. When singing, various vocal expressions are connected to phonetics, *the building blocks of all languages.*

Songs: Using songs and various music-centered activities, you can create a language-learning environment that is rich and multi-sensory. This environment will help them develop a deep awareness of the multiple nuances in phonetics.

Repetition and pattern recognition: Consider musical repetition and pattern recognition. Usually, songs are structured in a way that gives them a pattern, and the lyrics are often repeated. The pattern and repetition make it easy for your child to learn new words and remember phonemes (sounds) and graphemes (the written form of sound). Take the rhyme "Baa, Baa, Black Sheep." This rhyme involves repeating the sound "b," so it's easy for them to remember the "b" sound.

Stress and rhythm: These elements can be found in music and speech. Like in music, certain syllables are stressed, and intonation rules must be followed. Your child picks up on these with ease. The patterns help them pronounce and accentuate things correctly. When singing along to a song, they can clap or stomp in time with it. That helps them master the syllabic structure and what syllables to emphasize as they speak.

Rhyming and alliteration: Music involves rhyming and alliteration, so there's no better way to help your child than with music. They'll become more phonetically aware as they listen and sing along to songs that possess these elements. They'll notice that some sounds are similar and others aren't, which will help them speak better.

Melody and intonation: Songs are excellent because they're based on melody, which can help teach your child about intonation. Songs will have various pitches reminiscent of the rise and fall of voices in human speech. Think about how your voice rises at the end of a question or falls at the end of an instruction. Toddlers learn about these intonations and use them as they interact with others.

When you incorporate music into speech therapy, you'll get the best out of your child because they'll enjoy dancing and singing. Playing music converts the environment into a dynamic, interactive one.

Activities

78. **Sound It Out:** Get cards or toy blocks and label them with various phonemes. Let your toddler pick one up and pronounce the sound on it. You should have them articulate it clearly. To make this more advanced, you should combine blocks and have them pronounce the phonemes one after another before stringing them together.

79. **Funny Faces:** This game will help your toddler master moving their tongue, lips, and mouth to change the sounds they create. You both need to stand in front of the mirror for this one. Have them pronounce various phonemes. Model what they should do by exaggerating the mouth movements you need to pronounce each sound. Let your child notice how their faces change with each pronunciation in the mirror.

80. Word Hopscotch: You'll draw a hopscotch grid in your driveway, but this time, you've got to put various phonemes in each square. Your toddler has to hop on the phoneme as they pronounce it.

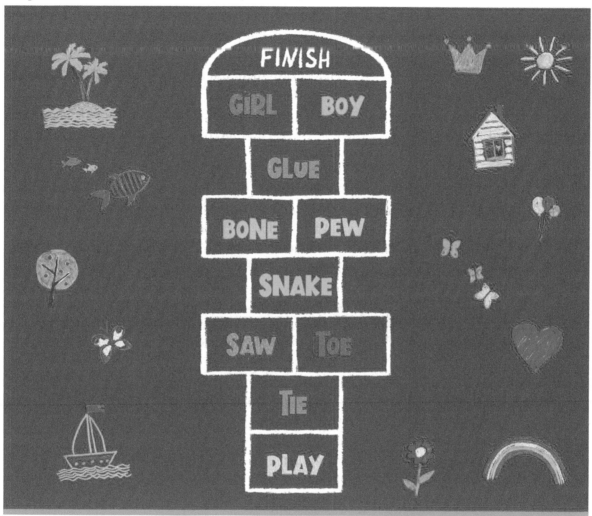

81. Phoneme Puzzler: Create easy puzzles where each piece matches a phoneme in a word. Let your toddler put the pieces together. As they grab a piece, they should pronounce the phoneme on it. When they've got all the pieces of a word together, let them pronounce each phoneme once more and then blend them.

BEGINNING SOUNDS

DIRECTIONS: Color the box that contains the beginning sound of each picture

h	l
n	t

k	m
n	e

u	e
o	a

z	b
r	d

r	w
g	c

m	s
n	t

PRONOUNCING PHONEMES

DIRECTIONS: Write the name of each word and the medial sound of each word. Follow the example.

word: *dog*

medial sound: *o*

word:

medial sound:

word:

medial sound:

word:

medial sound:

word:

medial sound:

word:

medial sound:

PRONOUNCING PHONEMES

Directions: Circle the correct letter to fill in the missing sound.

she☐p	a	e	f
g☐at	i	e	o
ap☐le	e	p	j
f☐og	n	d	r
☐og	b	p	d
chic☐en	r	k	c
☐uck	n	d	r

82. **Sound Switcheroo:** Start by pronouncing a simple word as clearly as possible. Then, have your toddler replace one of the sounds or phonemes with a different one to form a new word. You could have them replace the "b" in "bat" with a "c" to create a new word.

83. **Sound Cook-Off:** You're going to engage your toddler in baking. Your recipe should have ingredients that have the sounds you want them to work on in the words. As they hand each one to you, you should have them say each one and correct them gently if needed.

84. **Phonetic Matching Game:** This is a memory card game. Each card should have an image and a matching card with the word with the target sound you want your little one to practice. When your child finds a match, they should say the word aloud.

85. **Sound Artists:** You and your toddler should create art related to the words with the target phonemes you want them to work on. You can both take turns repeating these words. When you've done that, keep the artwork somewhere they can see it and use it to practice.

86. **Story Soundtrack:** Get your toddler's favorite books. Use them to create a soundtrack by assigning each major object and character with the target phoneme you want them to practice a unique sound in the story. You can drum on a table or use any musical instrument you have for this one. As you read the books, your child should make the sound you assigned each character or object and then say its name.

87. **Talking Puppy Show:** You can model proper sound pronunciation with puppets, so your child feels less pressured to be correct. You can create a story using the puppets with the target phonemes you want them to get right and then have them repeat those words or talk back to the puppet with them.

88. **Phonetic Pictionary:** This is like a regular Pictionary game, but there's a twist. Whatever words your toddler needs to learn is what they will work with. The pictures should contain words with the target sounds you want them to master. You can also get other people to try to guess what word it is so they can listen to how people pronounce it.

89. **Phonics Soundscapes:** You need a digital soundboard, which you can find online for free or as a mobile app. Whatever sounds your child needs to work on, assign one to a different button. Together, create stories that involve pressing a button to create the sound and have your toddler repeat after it.

90. **Sound Shapes Sculptures:** You need to work with clay or play dough to represent the various sounds you want your toddler to improve making. For example, the "S" sound could be depicted as a long winding snake, while the "M" sound could be shaped like two humps of a camel's back. While creating these shapes, have your toddler enunciate the sounds.

91. **Phonetic Yoga:** Assign yoga poses to various sounds. You could use the cobra pose to represent the "S" sound, while the tree pose could represent the "T" sound. While you move from one pose to the next, have your toddler say the sound aloud.

92. **Phonic Potion Mixer:** Set up a pretend play situation where you and your toddler act as magical sound wizards. For each target sound that needs work, there should be a potion or an ingredient that matches it. Your ingredients could be colored beads, colored water, pieces of paper, and shiny stars. You can mix all of these in a large bowl or pot, and as you do, have your child pronounce the sounds that correspond to each ingredient.

Reflection

Are there specific phonetic sounds your toddler has trouble with?

Which of the exercises was the best at helping them pronounce words more clearly?

How do you feel about the progress your little one is making with these exercises so far?

Chapter 7: Articulation and Pronunciation

Articulation is that aspect of language development that involves being able to move the various parts of your body, such as the palate, teeth, lips, and tongue, or articulators to create specific sounds called phonemes. The articulation of a sound depends on several things, including how you place your tongue and the shape of your lips. Regarding speech therapy for toddlers, the basic principles of articulation must be understood because that is how your toddler can speak clearly and accurately. Articulation enables you to produce sounds the way you do and use them to create words. Think about how children move from babbling and cooing when they're little to finally speaking their first words. This progression in speech development may seem random, but it isn't. The process is a result of your child learning to master their articulators. They learn how to make all these parts work together to create specific sounds.

For every sound, there is a specific placement movement. There's the part of your vocal tract where air flow will be blocked, and there's also a plethora of ways in which this airflow is blocked to create these sounds.

Then, there's whether a sound is *voiced* or *voiceless*. Think about the letter B. To pronounce it, you have to place your lips together. Then, you have to obstruct the airflow and vibrate your vocal cords. The letter P would be the same, except your vocal cords would not vibrate.

Always remember that your toddler is different from others. So, don't expect them to be at the same level of articulation as other children. Some are faster than others at developing articulate speech. If you want your child to improve at articulation, you need practice and time. Also, remember that several factors influence the process of mastering articulation. There's their physical development, how exposed they are to language, and possible hearing issues.

Articulation in speech is necessary to be understood and to speak clearly. If your child struggles to articulate words, they'll be difficult to understand, leading to frustration. It also means they may not enjoy socializing much because they realize people don't understand them. You may notice they're isolating themselves or finding it difficult to maintain friendships, let alone make new ones. Articulation is vital for literacy, too. When children correctly articulate sounds, they possess everything they need for phonemic awareness. It is an articulation that helps them realize that words have individual sounds. With this awareness, it's easier for them to learn reading and writing. So, early intervention when it comes to articulation issues is essential. Speech therapy can improve your little one's language skills through games and activities that help them master the movement of the articulators to speak clearly.

Hearing and Articulation

There is a connection between hearing and articulation. For your toddler to develop their speech, other processes are involved, and one of the most important ones is hearing. Consider the auditory feedback loop. This is a process in which your child can listen to the sounds they make as they read aloud and adjust how they articulate based on the sounds they get. It's a way of monitoring themselves to correct any mistakes they make. They continue to correct themselves until their sounds match the original sound modeled for them.

When your toddlers speak, they don't just make sounds. They are hard at work picking up the various sound waves. These waves will travel through the ear canal to the brain as electrical signals. In the center of the brain responsible for processing auditory information, these signals are then translated into something the child realizes is the sound they just made. This is where the feedback loop starts. If your child makes a sound that matches the original sound they are attempting to model in their brain, they'll keep pronouncing it that way. However, when the sound does not match, they may change how they articulate the word to pronounce it correctly.

The auditory feedback loop is a continuous one. Every time your child says something, they're listening to themselves. They're comparing what sounds they hear with what they meant to say. They're making adjustments as needed. That's why it's a feedback loop – a cycle where they must take action, reflect on their actions, and adjust as necessary.

If your little one is struggling with a hearing impairment, the process of the auditory feedback loop is disrupted. Your child will struggle with articulating correctly. It could be because they're not accurately hearing the sounds that they're saying. The result is a distortion as they compare the sounds they made with their internal model of the sound. Following that, they tend to misarticulate things. They'll distort sounds, replace them with other sounds, or omit them altogether.

Even when a toddler has normal hearing, the auditory feedback loop plays an important role. A speech-language pathologist will create strategies that help the child to pay attention to their manner of speaking. They may work with recording tools and playback tools. They could use amplification devices or just set up an environment that is quiet and free from distractions so your child can monitor themselves better.

Bilingualism and Articulation

Bilingualism is the ability to speak two different languages fluently. There are loads of benefits to be had from speaking two languages, especially in terms of education, social life, and cognitive performance. However, if your child is bilingual, they will need help with unique challenges when it comes to articulation. The obstacles your child will have to surmount are usually noticeable when they begin to understand the various complexities of language. They're mastering two different sets of phonetic rules that could vary significantly from each other. Every language has patterns of sounds that are unique to it. For your child to master each language, they must begin to grasp these patterns. This implies your bilingual child has a much larger phonetic sound bank than a child who only speaks one language.

Because your child has so much to learn in phonetics from two different languages, naturally, you'll notice that they have specific errors in pronunciation that their peers do not. They may substitute a sound from one language with a sound from the other. They may drop certain sounds just because it's the convention in the other language. These differences in pronunciation are something you can be reassured about. It's all a natural part of having your child learn two languages. So, do not assume immediately that your child is struggling with a speech impediment.

Bilingualism can affect your toddler's articulation and pronunciation skills regarding their accents or intonation patterns. Since all languages vary in stress, rhythm, and intonation, your child may apply the rules of one language to another. This is something to expect, particularly in the early stages when your child is still grasping language. Another challenge is that if you teach your child two languages with very different phonologies, they may struggle with articulating particular sounds in one language while doing better in the other. The letter R in Spanish is pronounced differently than R in English. If your child is learning both languages, it's natural to expect them to struggle adequately articulating this sound in each language.

Note that if you want your child to speak fluently in both languages, they may be better at one than the other. Their ability to be fluent in one language could shift with time depending on exposure and how often the language is used. If that's the case, you can expect their dominant language to influence how they pronounce and articulate things in the non-dominant language. Once more, there is nothing to be concerned about. These obstacles your child will face are usually transient and will pass. They're natural and nothing to be worried about. The older your child gets, and the more they are exposed to both languages, the better they'll become at telling the differences in phonetic roles of both languages.

Activities

93. **Phonic Jungle:** Get and hide several toys and objects around your home. These should start with the target sound you want your toddler to get better at articulating. Have them go on a "safari" to locate these items. Once they find them, have them say the item's name aloud.

94. **Articulation Artistry:** Your child should draw something connected to a word with the sound you want them to work on. For each stroke of the crayon, let them say the word aloud. Remember, repetition is essential for mastering language.

95. **Phonic Photoshoot:** You and your child should take turns taking pictures of items that start with a particular phoneme. Their job is to pronounce the object's name correctly before they can take a picture of it.

96. **Wacky Whispers:** You and your little one must mimic the target sound in a funny, exaggerated whisper.

97. **Word Chef:** You'll need a toy cooking set for this. Write down words on pieces of paper that contain the phoneme you want your toddler to get better at articulating. Pretend to add ingredients together, and then present your toddler with a piece of paper. They must read the word on it, and when they get it correctly, you can start cooking the next word.

Word chef can be played in a toy kitchen.

98. **Sound Sort:** Set out various pictures on the floor or a low table. Your toddler must arrange these pictures according to their beginning, middle, or last sounds. As they arrange the pictures, have them say the sound aloud.

99. **Phonetic Feasts:** When your toddler is having a meal, get them to name all the foods with the target sound they need to practice. Before taking a bite, they should repeat the word.

100. **Chatty Chores:** You and your toddler need to do chores in the house. As you do, name all the items used for the chores with the target sound. They need to repeat the word correctly.

101. **Phonic Fishing:** This is a fishing game you make up with paper fish and magnets. Label each of the fish with a word that has the target sound. Glue or tape a magnet on the back of the paper. Then, create a makeshift line by using a stick with a string tied at one end and a magnet tied at the end of the string. Get your child to go fishing for words. When the magnet picks up a fish, get them to say the word they caught.

102. **Supermarket Sounds:** You will play pretend to go shopping with your little one. Name every item with a target sound you want them to get correctly. Let them repeat the word to you as many times as they'd like.

103. **Articulation Athlete:** Create an obstacle course in your home. Make it fun and engaging with a bunch of colors and different sizes and textures of objects. At each station, have your child say a word that matches the target sound you want them to work on before they continue with the obstacle course.

104. **Sound Stacking:** As your toddler stacks blocks, get them to say a word with the target sound for each block they stack. The aim is to see how high your toddler can stack their tower while practicing sounds.

105. **Verse Voyage:** You and your toddler need to develop rhymes specifically containing the target sound they struggle with.

106. **Chatty Checkers:** If your child is old enough to understand checkers, play a game with them. As a rule, every player must correctly pronounce a word containing the sound that needs work before making a move.

Chatty checkers is just checkers with a twist.

107. **Phonic Puppets:** Get some puppets to act out a scene, but make sure this scene is full of words with the target sound. This way, your toddler can hear the sound repeatedly and improve at internalizing and replicating it correctly.

Reflection

Which of the articulation games was most fun for your toddler?

Did you find any of your their pronunciation challenges surprising?

What are your plans to assist your child with articulating their words better going forward?

Chapter 8: Enhancing Toddler Speaking and Listening

Speaking and listening are both linked to language development. It's this connection that helps you understand how your child can get better at communicating clearly and effectively. They master these skills simultaneously, and progress in one area is reflected in the other. Therefore, the feedback loop acts as reinforcement, rapidly propelling their progress with linguistics. Listening is the most basic requirement in acquiring a language. Before your child speaks, they pay attention to the various rhythms and sounds in the sentences the adults around them make. They're not listening passively. They learn a lot during this phase, including how to recognize voices. They're learning what each sound might imply. They're figuring out what specific phrases or words mean and finally developing the blueprint for them to speak.

Listening can help your toddlers with communication.
https://unsplash.com/photos/JrrWC7Qcmhs

Children will need their listening skills to communicate better when they begin to speak. They pick up on new words and sentence structures as they soak in the conversations around them. Your kid may have no clue what a "horse" means. After hearing it repeatedly in various situations, like when you read to them or when they're at a zoo, they will figure it out eventually and add that word to their vocabulary. So, paying attention when listening will influence how well your child learns to speak.

How Speaking Affects Listening

On the flip side, getting better at speaking does wonders for listening. When your child starts talking, they'll be more willing to participate in the conversations around them. They must pay close attention when asked questions, come up with the correct answers, and follow the conversation. You should encourage them to speak because that's how they get used to the differences between words and the sounds made.

As the child listens, they notice the sentence structures and the contextual differences in language. They could share with you about how they feel or what they think. In the process, they become more aware of constructing a sentence and how words can demonstrate various concepts. Their growing awareness of these things means they're getting better at listening and understanding the more complex nature of language.

Speaking is a great way to give your child instant feedback on their listening skills. When they don't pronounce something correctly, how others react to their error helps them learn where they went wrong.

Parent-Child Interactive Communication

Interacting with your child does wonders for their speech and listening skills. You can't afford to *not* communicate with them. Not only is this communication necessary for fostering a bond between you two, but it's also needed for them to be well-rounded socially, emotionally, and cognitively. You should have the best conversations with your child because those interactions allow them to copy good speaking and listening habits from you. They learn to be responsive as they connect with others. Overall, their language skills get a considerable boost.

Quality interactions are essential because, as their parent or primary caregiver, you're their first source of exposure to the language. So, by engaging in conversations with your child, you introduce them to all sorts of grammatical structures, conversation styles, and a more expansive vocabulary. The best conversations involve you letting your child take the reins. Get interested in what they're doing and how they're thinking.

When they can see how taken you are with them and how much you want to know what they're up to, they'll want to communicate with you even more. In turn, their speech will improve. Conversations with your little one are excellent chances to model what it's like to wait your turn in a conversation, which is necessary for active listening and interacting with other people.

Equally as important as high-quality interactions is responsive communication. This refers to how you respond to your child when they try to communicate with you. It's about your reactions, whether you speak, make a sound, facial expression, or gesture. By being responsive, you show your toddler you can tell they're trying to communicate, and you offer them feedback, encouraging them to keep trying.

When they point at a dog and say, "Dog," you can respond by saying, "Yes, that's a small, cute, white dog! Do you want to pet him?" This validates your child's desire and attempts to reach out to you, allowing you to teach them new words and more complex language structures. Practicing responsive communication can make your toddler feel more confident when speaking. They will want to try out more complex sentences.

Communicating with them responsively is a great way to model good listening and speaking habits. More than anyone else, you're the one your child looks to for cues on acting. They learn proper articulation, use a broader vocabulary, and speak using whole sentences. Also, they notice when you listen and learn to do the same when it's their turn to speak to you or when speaking with others. They also learn to develop responses that fit the message they're listening to. In this way, your child also learns empathy as they understand the world through others' eyes. They'll be more respectful when communicating with others, and their interactions will be meaningful.

Mindful Listening

Mindful listening is about being intentional when paying attention to sounds and verbal cues. It requires you to concentrate and participate actively during your interactions with your toddler. You need to understand what they're saying. You have to take in everything that comes to you in auditory form, from the emotional undertones to meaningful pauses, rhythms, and changes in tone. Once you've got all that down, you must respond thoughtfully. You should always create a space where your child feels they're understood. They should feel like whatever they have to share is valid.

Mindful listening can show your child what it's like to listen actively. You show them how to get rid of distractions and give all their focus only to what the other person is saying. You show them why they should make eye contact and how to perform other nonverbal communication cues, such as smiles and nods. As you listen mindfully, you reflect on what they share with you and ask for clarification when needed. To do this, paraphrase their words or ask them an open-ended question to encourage them to speak more. Ultimately, their vocabulary will be better for it.

Technology for Better Speaking and Listening

You can use technology to help your child improve speaking and listening to others. You should be present and monitor your toddler's progress. You can use many forms of technology to help them, such as children's podcasts, audiobooks, educational apps, and more.

Educational apps are great, as various apps are designed to help your child improve speaking and listening. They'll learn new vocabulary, new ways to put words together, pronounce them correctly, and other essential aspects of grammar and language. With the array of apps available, you have to choose the right ones for your child. For one thing, they must be age-appropriate. For another, you want something interactive that will engage your toddler's attention. It's better to pick an app that requires active participation instead of only needing your toddler to watch the screen and do nothing else. The best apps will have voice input and let your toddler touch and swipe the screen. These are important because they increase the child's autonomy and provide positive reinforcement and feedback when they get something right. Ensure you're always supervising your child so you're not inadvertently exposing them to questionable material. You also should be available to offer help when they need it.

Here are some of the best apps and sites you can use:

1. **ABCmouse** is a great preschool learning website offering a comprehensive learning program that greatly supplements your child's education. It's so fun for children that they typically never want to stop learning, and it's a worthwhile investment to help your child. You can even track their progress to see where they're doing well. You can sign up by visiting ABCmouse.com.

2. **PBS Kids Games** is a lovely app because it has many games your child will enjoy. Your child won't even realize they're getting a lesson as they use the app. It's constantly updated, so there's never a dull moment for your little one.

3. **Homer Learn and Grow** is an excellent app with a fun way of teaching all sorts of things, from reading to math. Your child will even learn about their social and emotional selves, which is excellent. You can also customize the learning experience to suit your child.

4. **Daniel Tiger's Grr-ific Feelings** will help your little one learn about their emotions and facial expressions. In learning positive and healthy ways to express themselves, they'll also master new words.

5. **Khan Academy Kids** is another app your toddler can enjoy as they learn to read, write, and improve their math and social-emotional skills. As of the time of writing, this app is free. On top of that, it's always kept fresh with new updates.

6. **Beck and Bo** is a lovely app that works with pretend play. The animations are beautiful. The app will transport your child to various everyday places like the library or grocery store and more exotic places like the jungle. Your child gets to put different objects in each scenario or learn new words as they learn what various items are called. Your child will expand their vocabulary as they work with this app.

7. **Epic** is a lovely app to help your child fall in love with reading. The platform has over 40,000 books, so you don't always have to visit the library. There are also foreign language books and quizzes so your child can become bilingual. You can try out the app for a month before you pay a monthly fee.

8. **Articulation Station** has many activities to help your kids learn how to say words and use them correctly in sentences. In no time, you'll see their speech skills getting better. The game has different stories, sounds, and levels with programs to help with problem sounds like S, L, and R. The app also offers voice recording, playback, and the ability to track data and take notes. The app makes it easy for your child to learn how to practice various sounds. The downside is only one letter comes free, while the rest have to be purchased individually. It's also not great for groups, so keep that in mind.

9. **Splingo** is a fun way for your child to learn to listen and sharpen their language skills, using amazing games set in a world with spaceships and aliens. It focuses on helping your child learn verbs, nouns, prepositions, and adjectives. This app works for a robust range of ages.

10. **Speech Tutor** has fantastic animated movies rendered in 2D, letting you see a side view of the scenes and a view from within the head as the tongue and other parts of the mouth work to create specific sounds. The app is designed to help your child learn how to properly produce sounds by correctly positioning their lips, tongue, and teeth. Your child can also record their replication of the sound and play it back to see how well they've done.

11. **LAMP Words for Life** is a great one if your child has autism. It teaches your children through the Language Acquisition through Motor Planning (LAMP) therapy method. The app is lovely for children learning how to communicate and even older children with some language skills but want to do better.

12. **Proloquo2Go** is a lovely app to help children who cannot speak properly improve their communication and language skills. You can set it up to match your toddler's accessibility and vocabulary needs. You get to pick from at least 100 text-to-speech voices that sound incredibly natural, with none of that "uncanny valley" sounding voice typical of certain apps. You may need to help your child work with the app as the interface is a bit complex.

Audiobooks are great for your child's listening and speaking skills, too. They're wonderful for helping them keep up with a narrative until the end. They must follow the story and pay attention. These audiobooks are also recorded with proper pronunciation and articulation, so you can use them to help your child develop these skills – especially with the variety of voices, speech rates, tones, and accents they're recorded with. Their ears will be gradually tuned to pick up on the nuances and subtleties in language. Also, you can pause the audiobook and talk about the story so far, ask your child questions, and get them to predict the next scene. In this way, you boost their comprehension skills.

Children's podcasts blend entertainment and education beautifully. They allow your child to learn much about the world and improve their vocabulary. They're also great for critical thinking. Like audiobooks, podcasts show your child how to understand the spoken word and keep up with complex arguments and narratives. You can also use podcasts to engage them in conversation so they can share their thoughts and feelings on the discussed topic.

Activities

108. **Sound Bounce:** Make a unique sound or say a word. Your toddler has to echo it accurately and as quickly as they can. This way, you have a "tip-tap" rhythm going on. If your child is a little slow with it, don't be hard on them. Encourage them. You can build on this game from words to phrases and short sentences.

109. **Question Quest:** This conversational game involves you and your child asking each other questions. Choose open-ended questions. They must respond appropriately and pay attention because each answer will lead to the next question.

110. **Story Builder:** Start a story, then wait for your toddler to give you a word. Continue the story using that word. Then it's their turn. Let them start a story, and then you supply them with a word they must continue the story using that word.

111. **Word Seeker:** Say a word, and let your child find something around you that matches that word somehow.

112. **Expression Exchange:** Say a phrase with an emotion. Your child should say the same word with the same emotional tone.

113. **Chatter Charades:** Take turns acting as different characters for the other person to guess what's happening. However, you're not going to use actual words. You will act out different emotions in each scenario while speaking gibberish. When you've finished, let your child come up with an explanation for what happened in the scene.

114. Story Spinners: Get a wheel and put different words on it. Let your toddler spin it, and when it stops, they have to tell a story about the word in one minute. Wherever they stop, they have to spin the wheel again and pick up the story with the new word they land on.

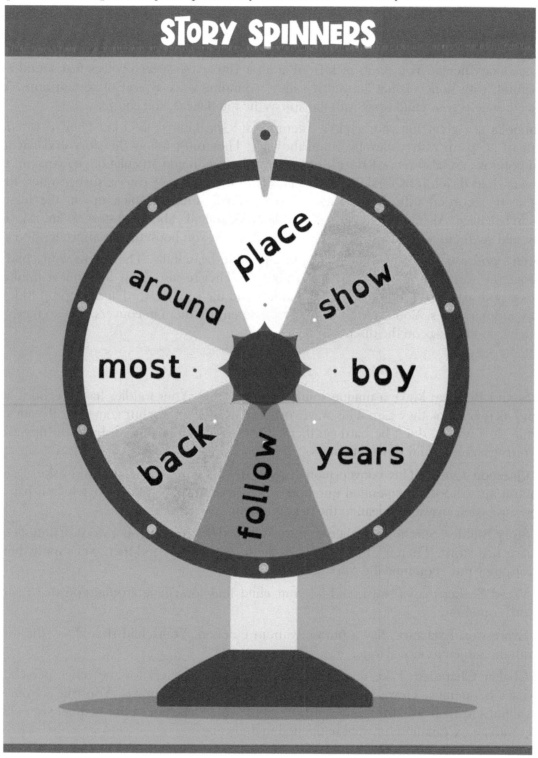

115. Picture Pairs: Get pairs of picture cards. Describe what's on a card, but don't show your child. Instead, let them look for the card that matches what you've got from the rest of the pile.

PICTURE PAIRS

CASTLE	KING	QUEEN	KNIGHT
PRINCE	PRINCESS	BUFFOON	CARRIAGE
CASTLE	KING	QUEEN	KNIGHT
PRINCE	PRINCESS	BUFFOON	CARRIAGE

116: Rhyme Tales: Instead of coming up with rhyming words, you and your toddler need to develop stories or sentences that end with a rhyming word. If the word is "hat," they could say, "I saw a man wearing a hat," and you could respond, "He was running away from a rat."

117. Sound Snap: To do this, use sounds from real life, like a door closing or a running tap. Set up a grid with pictures of the objects and creatures that make your chosen sounds. Play the sounds one after another, and let your toddler spot and cover the correct picture on their bingo grid.

118. Mimic Mystery: One of you should act out something while making a sound. You could hop like a frog and croak. The other person has to copy the action and sound. Have your toddler identify what you're mimicking and take your turn to guess what they're doing.

119. Doodle Dialogue: Take turns drawing aspects of a story on paper and, as you draw, narrate it.

120. Action Auction: In the style of an auctioneer, list many actions playfully. "I have one twirl, one hop, and one squat. Do I hear two twirls?" Then, your toddler should bid by choosing the actions, repeating the words, and doing the actions.

121. Rhythm Rumble: Use any musical instrument to make an easy beat. No instrument? No problem. You can clap or bang pots and pans together. Your toddler needs to repeat the rhythm however they can.

122. Banana Boat Adventure: Get your toddler to imagine the living room is an ocean and the couch is a banana boat. Throw cushions, socks, toys, stuffed animals, and anything else into the "water" around your boat. Your toddler needs to rescue them. How? Describe what you're looking at, and when your toddler correctly figures out which object you're describing, they can pick it up and bring it back to the boat.

Reflection

On a scale of 1 to 10, how would you rate your toddler in terms of their listening skills?

Which of the games made your child more enthusiastic and confident about speaking?

Which activity from this chapter would you like to use more often?

Chapter 9: The Power of Reading

Part of childhood development is early reading exposure, and you can't afford to ignore it. This gives your child a foundation to develop linguistically, cognitively, and eventually academically. The early years of your little one's life are critical for learning languages because their brain is very plastic and open to learning new ideas. During the early years, a child's brain absorbs everything and anything around it.

When you introduce your child to reading, you teach them through words. You're offering them a vibrant source of language. This source is full of stories that captivate their mind, and books have variety in vocabulary and sentence structure. As you read aloud to your toddler, you teach them that language has structure and rhythm. They pick up on nuances in grammar and the way you appear to sing with your words. Reading to your child is an excellent way to help them understand how to string their sentences together. On top of that, children's books are deliberately written in a way that offers them a variety of words they can absorb and use.

Reading can teach your toddler that language has structure and rhythm.
https://www.pexels.com/photo/girl-in-red-dress-sitting-on-bed-reading-book-3661473/

As your child seeks more complicated books, they gain a massive advantage over those who do not read. Books possess complex sentences and more words than your child may be exposed to in daily conversation. You teach your child new ideas and words as you read to them. They understand these words with time, master their pronunciations, and get to understand how to use them in the correct situation or context. By reading to them as early as possible, they will understand the language far more comprehensively than others not exposed to reading. Early reading is an excellent way for your toddler to master the various structures and language. Conversational speech is usually more straightforward. However, books are far more complex and descriptive. This is excellent because it shows them how to develop their speaking and writing styles as they grow older.

Reading will open up your child's mind to various sounds of speech. As a result, they get better at noticing the differences in phonology between languages. It'll also teach your child to love the many worlds only a book can create. It fuels the fire of curiosity within them. It encourages them to work with their imagination and to understand that there are no limits to what they can create.

Additionally. reading is great for teaching empathy. Your child learns about different characters in different situations, going through different issues. When you and your child read aloud with each other, you have an opportunity to bond with them. They will feel safe and nurtured. Then, it's much easier for your child to develop emotionally, socially, and linguistically.

Exposing your child to books early has other benefits. Children who begin reading when they're little are likelier to do well in academics and their careers later in life. They have a much broader vocabulary and greater mastery of language skills by the time they enter school. Your child will naturally be ahead of the curve because you have given them access to the magical world of books.

There are so many facets to letting your toddler learn to read early. It's not necessarily just about knowing how to read or improving speech and language skills. It's about giving them a fighting chance to succeed in life. It's about sparking within them a love for story and a thirst for knowledge.

Storytelling: The Art of Narrative Skills

Storytelling involves narrative skills, and by using this tool, you help your child with reading and take their speech therapy sessions to the next level. Narration is about using descriptive language to talk about events and things or to craft stories. It's a powerful, necessary linguistic skill that requires your toddler to use the correct vocabulary, proper syntax, narrative structure, and sequencing. Storytelling is immersive. Getting your child to be able to understand and tell stories will go a long way toward endearing them to others in life. Through stories, they can even persuade others to see things their way when needed.

There's a structure to stories. Typically, they start at the beginning, where the reader or listener is introduced to the characters and their world. Next, there's the middle, where the meat of the story happens with the twists and turns, highs and lows, and all the problems. Then, there's the end of the story, where the problem is solved. This is the most basic narrative structure. By grasping it, your child will find it easy to understand stories. They'll be able to predict what might come next, which further lends to their immersion and enjoyment of the story. With time, they can sort out their thoughts to express themselves coherently. Their expressive language skills become elevated as a result.

Since stories are sequential, your toddler must master sequencing skills. In other words, they should be able to talk about whatever events they witnessed in an order that makes sense to be clearly understood. Stories are an excellent way for them to master the skills as they pay attention when others read or share their tales. You can have them retell the stories they know in their own words to help them put things in order. Through stories, your toddler begins to understand that there's more than one way to see the world. They can learn to accommodate other viewpoints, responses, reactions, and emotions. Naturally, they become more empathetic, and their social skills improve.

In speech therapy, storytelling is a great way to engage your toddler's attention while having them practice their language and speech skills. If they're struggling with the language, stories are lovely tools to motivate them to participate in therapy actively. Stories give all the activities toddlers have to partake in more meaning. Speech therapists know how powerful stories are for practicing speech-related skills like articulation. Also, kids' stories incorporate rhymes and repeat phrases often. As already discussed, rhyming and repetition are excellent for helping kids master various sounds to produce speech correctly. Since phrases are repeated, your toddler can take part in reading the story. As they read, they feel more confident in their use of the language and more willing to practice.

Selecting Age-Appropriate Reading Materials

You have to pick material that's appropriate for your little one. You have to think not only about the content of the books but also about the complexity of the vocabulary and language. Think about how long the book is and the sort of imagery that goes along with the text. Your child will find it helpful if the text is clear and simple. The language should be concise. Sentences have to be short. If you notice a book has rhymes and repeated phrases, that's a great choice because they'll become predictable to your child and help them to anticipate what comes next so they can take an active part in the story.

When it comes to content, the book has to be relatable. The themes should be intricately connected to your child's everyday experiences. This way, they'll better grasp the story, and their language development will go up several notches. The best books are the kind that talk about colors, shapes, animals, and everyday routines they're used to doing. Also, choose a book that engages their sense of sight. You should go for books that have large, colorful, bright, and brilliant pictures so you can keep their attention. Your toddler will enjoy These kinds of books immensely and be happy to immerse themselves in fully — especially if they know nothing about text just yet. Pictures are explanatory. Your child can look at one, put two and two together, and understand what's happening. The pictures are also a great way to spark a conversation with them. You can have them talk about what they assume might come next so they can use expressive language skills.

Book length is another thing to consider. Children don't have the best attention spans, so you should choose something short enough to keep them invested in the story from start to finish. If you choose ones that are too long, they may feel bored or overwhelmed before you reach the end. You don't want this to happen because they may conclude that there's nothing enjoyable about reading.

A final point thing to consider is a book's durability. You have a child. Children love to rip things up, put them in their mouths, or smear them. They haven't yet learned how to care for or handle things gently. You can trust they'll be as rough with their book as they are with their other things. So, you should always look for sturdy books. Opt for books made from hard cardboard, fabric books, and any other kind that will survive your toddler's drooling, teething, and throwing.

Activities

123. Texture Tales: Let your toddler enjoy interacting with fabric books that have various textures. They'll enjoy the story because it's interactive.

124. Sound Emulation: Read books with animal characters and, at the end of the book, have your child emulate the animal sounds you make for each one.

125. Weather Windows: Read weather stories to them whenever you're experiencing the corresponding weather. If it's raining, read them a book about rain.

126. Pop-up Pantomime: Get some pop-up books, and have your child re-enact the characters' actions.

Pop-up books transport a child to a 3-dimensional world of wonder.
Thuwirawat, CC BY-SA 4.0 <https://creativecommons.org/licenses/by-sa/4.0>, via Wikimedia Commons
https://commons.wikimedia.org/wiki/File:Bangkok_pop-up_book.jpg

127. Temperature Tales: Read stories about heat and cold. As you do this, you can adjust the room's temperature as needed. This will make those stories' words and experiences stick in their minds.

128. Shadow Stories: Use a flashlight and shadow puppets to tell a story. Your child will enjoy this one immensely.

129. Flavorful Fables: Prepare any meals or snacks that come up in the book you're reading to your child. You can enjoy these snacks while you read.

130. Scented Stories: If you have essential oils, and there are scents or smells mentioned in the story you and your toddler are enjoying, you can have them smell what each scent is like.

Essential oils can make reading more interesting to toddlers.
https://www.pexels.com/photo/variety-of-essential-oils-6707634/

131. Color Chronicles: As you read your toddler books centered on color, you should show them colorful objects that match.

132. Rhythm Rhymes: Read rhythmic books to your toddler. You can make things more interesting by clapping or tapping in time with the words.

133. Nature Narratives: You can read your toddler stories about nature while in the park.

134. Artsy Adventures: Once you and your toddler have finished reading a book, you can create art based on the scenes or the characters your toddler finds fascinating.

135. Costume Chronicles: Once you and your child have finished a story, dress up as the characters and act out the scenes. Do your best to say the lines as they are in the book, or at least incorporate words your toddler may struggle with so they can practice. Also, stay in character until the end of the activity.

136. Musical Mysteries: As your toddler reads a story aloud, you can play music or instruments with them. You can play them when the story has emotional peaks or lows to make things more interesting.

137. Bouncy Ballads: As you read, you can bounce a ball or tap your foot in time with the sentences. Doing this will make your toddler more phonemically aware.

Reflection

What are your thoughts on reading to improve your toddler's speech?

Which of the reading games did they enjoy the most?

Which of the reading strategies do you think should be an everyday thing for your child?

Chapter 10: Speech Impediments and How to Overcome Them

Usually, children are prepared to learn languages as soon as they are born. However, they must learn the language their family and immediate environment use. Language learning is a process that requires patience and time. Since every child is different, speech and language development milestones won't occur simultaneously. Children tend to have issues pronouncing certain words, sounds, and sentences as they learn. However, you can expect your little one to have adjusted to using language at about five years of age.

As a parent or a caregiver, it is your responsibility to help your child master their language during their formative years. Children can pick up on language by listening to others and practicing what they hear. Even the youngest ones pay attention to the words others repeat around them. You'll find them responding to specific sounds and noises that they hear. Children's language and cognitive abilities become more robust when exposed to more words. You help your child in many ways, such as responding to all their little coos, babbles, gurgles, gestures, and any other sounds they make. You can also repeat after them, talk about everything they can see, ask open-ended questions, tell stories, sing songs, etc.

Sometimes, however, your child may be struggling with speech impediments. A speech impediment is when your child can't speak and be understood by others. It's a sign of certain developmental or physical factors. When you overlook speech impediments, it can be hard for them to master literacy skills like reading and writing. It also makes it challenging for them to integrate into society. Certain speech impediments, such as a cleft palate or a tongue tie, will require surgery to address. However, speech therapies are often more than enough for most speech impediments a child could struggle with.

Types of Speech Impediments

There are various kinds of speech impediments, but the most common are stuttering, dysarthria, apraxia, and ankyloglossia.

Stuttering

Stuttering affects the way your child speaks in terms of rhythm and flow. They make sounds they do not intend to, pause, or struggle with anything that prevents them from speaking smoothly. There are various kinds of stuttering. There is developmental stuttering, which tends to happen because of a neurodevelopmental disorder. Persistent stuttering is when it continues even into adult years. Acquired stuttering is developed due to injury or illness that affects your cognitive functions.

Stuttering is a fluency disorder that can happen to anyone but is often more likely to affect male children. Developmental stuttering is a childhood condition that begins as early as age two or seven at the latest. On average, it starts at about age three, and 95% of children begin struggling with this before they reach four. Childhood stuttering is something that 1% to 2.4% of children struggle with.

Signs of Stuttering

1. You know your child is struggling with stuttering if you notice that they keep repeating certain syllables or sounds. Often, the repetition is on the first syllable of the word.

2. You may also notice they tend to draw out certain sounds or syllables as they get stuck on them. They may pause in the middle of a word for longer than necessary.

3. There's also another form of pausing called blocking. In this case, your little one may pause silently, or they may insert a filler word like "ah" or "um."

4. Word switching is another sign of stuttering. This is when your child stutters in a word or phrase and then chooses a different one to get around the blockage.

5. If you also notice that your child tends to place far too much emphasis on a particular word or part of one, or if saying it tends to make them feel tense, this could be a sign that they're struggling.

6. Another tendency is to repeat a specific word that has just one syllable.

7. You may also notice spasms, particularly in the arms, shoulders, neck, and face.

8. Sometimes, when stuttering, your little one may develop specific actions or tics. They may blink excessively, avoid eye contact, grimace, or clench their fists.

9. Usually, if the child is feeling stressed, anxious, excited, or tired, their stuttering worsens.

10. It can also worsen when they're talking about complicated topics they still need to grasp or when it's one they've never encountered before. When they feel relaxed or rested, they don't stutter as much. You might also notice that they don't stutter when singing or speaking to a pet.

Ways to help your child stop stuttering:

- Speak slowly. Take care to pronounce each word correctly and clearly. Your child will copy this and get better as they stutter less.

- Praise them whenever they say something fluently. Stop pointing it out when they stutter.

- Work with a speech therapist. They can give you the best strategies to help your child.

Unfortunately, stuttering can cause a host of mental health issues. It can be a source of shame, embarrassment, and frustration if you do not help your child while they're still young. Sometimes, a stutter could result from family history, genetic mutations, or differences in brain structure. The best way to diagnose this condition is to work with a professional speech therapist.

Ankyloglossia or Tongue-Tie

Tongue-tie is a condition where someone's tongue is too closely connected to the floor of their mouth because of a thin strip of tissue. When that strip is shorter than it should be, the tongue's movements are restricted. This is a common condition for young children and newborns. It is connected to breastfeeding issues and speech issues. This condition is congenital.

There is a difference between the anterior tongue tie and the posterior tongue tie. The former happens in the front of the mouth, close to the tip of a tongue, just behind the lower gums and teeth. It resembles a thin web. The posterior tongue tie is also known as a hidden tongue tie. This one is further back in the mouth, where the floor meets the tongue, so it's difficult to see. Note that interior tongue ties are far more common than posterior ones.

This condition affects at least 10% of newborns. Sometimes, a child may learn how to work with it the older they get. However, if the tongue tie is too problematic, it's best to address it as early as possible because symptoms can worsen with age. Sometimes, the condition can be mild. Other times, it can be quite severe.

Signs of Tongue-Tie

1. Your child finds it hard to stick their tongue out. If they can, it can't go past their lower front teeth. They may also be unable to lift their tongue to touch their upper front teeth.

2. You may notice a V shape or a little heart at the tip of your toddler's tongue.

3. When a newborn struggles with tongue-tie, it could lead to latching when it comes to breastfeeding, breastfeeding for far too long, constantly feeling hungry, trouble with weight, and a constant clicking sound when your child feeds.

More often than not, this condition is so mild that the symptoms will not affect daily life.

Ways to help your tongue-tied child:

- Work with a specialist to develop tongue exercises to help your toddler.

- If the tongue-tie is severe, they may need a frenectomy. This procedure is simple: the frenulum (the tissue that ties your toddler's tongue) is cut to give your child more wiggle room to speak.

- If a frenectomy doesn't help much or the tongue-tie isn't that terrible, you could use speech therapy to help your child articulate words better.

Apraxia

This neurological condition affects some children as they try to master language. They know what to say but can't find the words. This condition can happen to any child. It's not clear yet what causes it. A telltale sign of apraxia is when they cannot easily chew or use a straw. They may also struggle to take a drink from a cup or even process what they feel when they swallow.

If your child is of school age and struggles with spelling, writing, and reading, they may be dealing with apraxia. This could be another sign of trouble with fine motor skills, such as picking up tiny objects or drawing.

Childhood apraxia of speech is rare and only affects one to two out of every thousand children in the United States. It makes it difficult for children to communicate effectively with words. They can't move their mouths as needed to accurately produce the sounds that make up the words. So, it doesn't matter that they know what they want to say; they just can't say it. While your child may be unable to speak because of apraxia, it is possible that they also struggle with getting their lips, tongue, and mouth to work together. Some children who have childhood apraxia of speech struggle with eating, but more often than not, the only thing affected is speech. To treat this condition, the speech therapist must address the various movements the toddler must learn to create sounds properly. So, treatment involves using augmentative communication or gesture communication. It all comes down to how severe their diagnosis is.

Signs of Apraxia

1. They are unable to enunciate different vowels and consonants. So, they may say "pie" instead of "bye."
2. You will also notice that their voice does not rise and fall in pitch when speaking.
3. When pronouncing words, they prefer simple words, as in ones with just a single vowel.
4. Also, they may master a word but quickly forget it because it's too difficult to use. You'll also notice that they drop certain sounds from words.

Ways to help your child with apraxia:

- Intensive speech therapy is an excellent solution to help your child with speech.
- Multisensory feedback involves working with a mirror so they can see how their mouth moves and compare it to yours. It also means working with touch to feel for vibrations in voiced sounds. You can also tap objects rhythmically to model how the sound should be pronounced.
- Augmentative and Alternative Communication (AAC) is useful when communication is extremely tough. It involves using devices like picture boards, speech generators, and apps that can help your child communicate. AAC isn't a permanent fix but a supplement for speech therapy.

To diagnose this condition, you'll need the help of a speech therapist. They will learn about your child's history and whatever medical issues they may be struggling with. They'll test their oral motor skills, hearing, and intonation. They'll check for any signs of weak mouth muscles and how well they can enunciate vowel and consonant sounds. They'll also see whether they can make non-speech oral motor movements such as smiling, rounding their lips, blowing, and quickly moving their mouth.

Overcoming Speech Impediments

Note that you can't predict your child will have a speech impediment, let alone prevent it. You are better off speaking with your child's healthcare provider whenever you realize they have issues with speaking. Your healthcare provider will see if there's anything to be concerned about and recommend actions for you to take to assist your child.

It's natural to wonder if you can fix a speech impediment. Understand that fixing these impediments requires various treatments. Generally, speech therapy will do wonders for your child's speech and language skills. This is why early intervention is necessary. If you feel like there's something off, don't put it off. You must remember that whatever course of action the therapist recommends, be prepared to wait for changes to occur. Be patient and understanding with your child. You're more likely to see results if you give them ample time without putting pressure. Here are other things to do to help your child with speech impediments:

1. Play the speech games in this book with your toddler each day. Pick the games that will suit their level of comprehension and language skills.

2. Do not repeat or copy your child's speech errors.

3. Read to them each day.

4. Listen carefully so you can spot issues.

5. Work closely with their speech therapist and teachers.

Reflection

Have you identified any speech impediments your child may have?

Which of the exercises in the book so far have tremendously reduced the effects of those impediments?

What books or reading styles might you introduce to your toddler to help them?

Bonus Section

Here are 15 more games you can play with your child to help them with their speech issues.

138. Vocal Vocations: Dress up and role-play as various professionals. Ideally, you should have a scripted dialogue that you can use to help your child become more fluent.

139. Travel Talk: You need a globe or a map of the world. Get your child to imagine flying to various countries and discuss the experiences they would have at famous landmarks.

140. Smelly Speech: For this exercise, blindfold your toddler. Then, get them to smell various food items and let them guess what they are.

141. Crunchy Conversations: Set up a snack picnic. It should be full of crunchy foods like pretzels, chips, and carrots. You and your toddlers should then talk about the sounds these foods make.

Crunchy foods can help toddlers with sound.
https://unsplash.com/photos/S4PC4ScKwKg

142. Whispering Wallets: Go on an imaginary shopping spree with your child. However, you must both whisper. This is a great way to teach them how to articulate while controlling the volume of their voice.

143. Puppet Pronunciations: Help your toddler practice various words and sounds with hand puppets. Instead of speaking directly to them, speak to them through the puppets.

144. Tasty Tongue Twisters: Come up with food-related tongue twisters. Make them fun and exciting. Think about the famous tongue twister that goes, "Peter Piper picked a peck of pickled peppers," and let that inspire you. This is an excellent way for your toddler to master articulation and fluency.

145. Musical Mumbling: Play music your toddler isn't familiar with and get them to hum or mumble the lyrics. It will make them pay close attention to the lyrics until they master them.

146. Sensory Sentences: Create a sensory bin full of objects of different sizes, shapes, and textures. Your child must stick a hand in and describe what the objects look like based on their feelings. When they pull the object from the bag, get them to say a complete sentence about it.

147. Animal Antics: You and your little one should take turns making animal sounds and guessing what the other person is imitating.

148. Throwing Thoughts: For this exercise, you need a bean bag or a softball that you and your toddler can throw back and forth. As you throw the ball, say a word or sentence. They should do the same as they throw it back to you.

149. Luminous Language: You and your child should be in a dim or dark room for this one. You'll need a flashlight. Use the light to highlight objects or toys for your child to describe or name.

150. Bubbly Words: Blow bubbles. Before your child pops one, they must say a specific sound or word.

Bubbly words will make learning more exciting.

151. Sunny Sentences: On a sunny day, you and your toddlers should go out and talk about the sun. You can talk about how bright it is, how warm it is, and how it suddenly gets cooler when the clouds obstruct it.

Bonus Activity:

Breezy Balloons: Inflate a balloon and let it fly. As you do, try to mimic the whooshing sound it makes and talk about it. Inflate the balloon again. This time, allow your toddler to let it fly. Let them try to copy the sound and talk about what they observed about the balloon or its sound as the air escapes.

Conclusion

When the world of language opens up to your toddler, it beckons their little hearts to learn how to use words to paint the inner landscape of their thoughts and emotions for others to witness and understand. Language is a powerful gift, one that your little one deserves to have. There's much to discover as they learn how to deftly weave words together to let you know they're hungry, tired, or don't enjoy the broccoli you keep trying to feed them. With all this in mind, this book has been written to help your toddler communicate clearly and with ease.

The point of this book is to give parents, caregivers, and child mental health experts the tools they need to help toddlers make the most of their language development journey. This journey goes beyond learning how to say words. It's about the ability to express themselves, connect meaningfully with others, make sense of their thoughts, and use words to be creative.

Language development is essential for your toddler. They have a curious mind that soaks things up like a sponge, so if they are struggling with speech impediments right now, that doesn't mean they're not learning or getting better. You just need to be patient with them. Be encouraging. When they get things right, celebrate them as if they just climbed Mount Everest — because they might as well have. Do all you can to ensure their environment is rich in language so you can channel their natural curiosity toward words, their meanings, and how they can be strung together to create newer meanings.

The activities in this book are efficient at getting your toddler to speak clearly and confidently. With time, your love, patience, and support, your toddler will thrive in a world full of words. Now that you've learned a fair bit from this book, it's time to get to work. You can give your child an edge in the world, fortifying their linguistic prowess. Practice with them, and they'll be so proficient that one day, with every word, phrase, and sentence they make, it will feel like a real accomplishment.

Check out another book in the series

References

Boynton, S. (1993). Barnyard Dance. Workman Publishing Company.

Bowen, C. (2015). Children's Speech Sound Disorders (2nd ed.). Wiley-Blackwell.

Dresner, M. (2017). The Speech Teacher's Handbook: A Parent's Guide to Speech and Language. Molly Dresner.

Fey, M. E., Warren, S. F., Brady, N., Finestack, L. H., Bredin-Oja, S. L., Fairchild, M., Sokol, S., & Yoder, P. J. (2006). Early effects of responsivity education/prelinguistic milieu teaching for children with developmental delays and their parents. Journal of Speech, Language, and Hearing Research.

Girolametto, L., Pearce, P. S., & Weitzman, E. (1996). Interactive focused stimulation for toddlers with expressive vocabulary delays. Journal of Speech and Hearing Research.

Katz, K. (2003). Counting Kisses: A Kiss & Read Book. Little Simon.

Kumin, L. (1994). Intensive early intervention for children with Down syndrome: Implications for speech-language pathologists. American Journal of Speech-Language Pathology.

Numeroff, L. J., & Bond, F. (1985). If You Give A Mouse A Cookie. HarperCollins Publishers.

Paul, R., &Norbury, C. F. (2012). Language disorders from infancy through adolescence: Listening, speaking, reading, writing, and communicating (4th ed.). Elsevier Mosby.

Priddy, R. (2011). First 100 Words Board Book Box Set. Priddy Books US.

Rescek, S. (2007). Hickory Dickory Dock And Other Favorite Nursery Rhymes. Tiger Tales.

Roberts, M. Y., & Kaiser, A. P. (2011). The effectiveness of parent-implemented language interventions: A meta-analysis. American Journal of Speech-Language Pathology.

Rossetti, L.M.(2001). Communication Intervention: Birth to Three (2nd ed.). Singular Publishing Group.

Scanlon,K.(2012). My Toddler Talks: Strategies and Activities To Promote Your Child's Language Development .CreateSpace Independent Publishing Platform.

Scherer N.J., &Olswang L.B.(1989). Using structured discourse as a language intervention technique with autistic children. Journal of Speech and Hearing Disorders.

Tannock R., &Girolametto L.(1992). Reassessing parent-focused language intervention programs In S.F. Warren & J.Reichle (Eds.), Causes and effects in communication and language intervention. Baltimore: Paul H.BrookesPublishing Co.

Warren S.F., & Yoder P.J.(1998). Facilitating the transition from prelinguistic to linguistic communication In A.M. Wetherby, L.B.Watson,&B.M.Schatz(Eds.), Transition in prelinguistic communication. Baltimore: Paul H. Brookes Publishing Co.

Watt, F.,&Wells, R.(1999). That's Not My Puppy. Usborne Publishing Ltd.

Willems,M.(2005). The Pigeon Has Feelings Too! Hyperion Books for Children.

Wood, A.,&Wood, D.(1984). The Napping House. HMH Books for Young Readers.

Made in the USA
Las Vegas, NV
10 January 2024

84189412R00050